EMOTIONAL

EATING

S.O.S.!

NATALIA ROSE

AUTHOR OF *THE RAW FOOD DETOX DIET*

Also by Natalia Rose:
The Raw Food Detox Diet
Raw Food Life Force Energy
The New Energy Body
Detox 4 Women
The Rose Cleanse

For more information about Natalia Rose,
visit www.detoxtheworld.com

For all my brothers and sisters on the journey back to wholeness.

What is this madness
That makes my motor run
And my legs too weak to stand
I go from sadness
To exhilaration
Like a robot at your command

—from "Automatic" by The Pointer Sisters

Contents

Note to Reader

Have you noticed that the two major obsessions of our culture, food and physical attractiveness, are unavoidably linked? In our culture, they betray each other constantly.

I wrote this book in honor of those of you who have spent too much of your lives—your thoughts, your emotions, your energy, your efforts, your resources, and your time—wrestling with the conundrum of food and body image in our world. Part nurturer, part enemy, food has been a source of great puzzlement for you. Emotional eating and poor body image have cast a dark shadow over your life for too long. It is my sincerest wish to help you gain clarity and freedom from this conundrum once and for all!

Your confidence in me with regard to this highly personal and deeply nuanced subject matter is a great inspiration. I wish to emphasize that I am not a trained therapist. The insights and guidance I offer come from a wealth of experience, along with extensive self-education in the art of soul-retrieval. It took me the better part of ten years to overcome the traps of my own emotional eating. I've discovered that those who chart their own way out of the labyrinth can often offer vital guidance to fellow travelers through this rough terrain.

What you'll find in the following pages is a serious inquiry into the forces that drive us to engage in self-destructive behavior; then we will culminate with a practical plan—a series of steps and exercises that I have found to be highly effective—for the journey back to balance.

How will you know if you are in fact healing? You will experience real, tangible, measurable change. Your thought patterns, behaviors, and inclinations will become distinctly life-generating. You will undergo a literal and a spiritual metamorphosis. You will dig deep to find the points of brokenness and shame that have undermined you all your life, and you will begin to recover your power, your freedom, your wholeness. As you undergo this metamorphosis, your life will unfold and take flight, and you will finally feel the rush of being truly alive.

Here's to your flight to freedom!

Natalia

Introduction

Overeating and emotional eating are almost always synonymous. Emotional eating is a serious illness. If left untreated, it can lead to many other serious physical and emotional illnesses. Yet, strangely, as the huddled masses dig their graves with their teeth (to borrow from an old French proverb), the truths about emotional eating are droned out by the dietary white noise of weight-loss fads and fuzzy nutritional science.

Needless to say, the popular approaches to health and diet are profoundly misguided. If the very fabric of a garment were inexplicably deteriorating, would a needle and thread do any good? Not remotely! Similarly, there is no quick medical fix for reversing the deterioration of our emotional and physical structures. The illnesses and disorders that run rampant among us today call for much more than modern medicine. We cannot begin to heal until we begin with a paradigm of wholeness.

Countless victims of illness and their advocates are desperate to find cures that remain elusive. Meanwhile, few people realize that these illnesses and disorders are not only easy to understand, but completely reversible in most cases with a natural, holistic approach to healing. This is true of many cases of autism, Alzheimer's, cancer, asthma, MS, IBS, and nearly everything in between.

There is a widespread emotional and physiological auto-destruction (self-destruction) taking place that is going virtually undetected by professionals and lay people alike, because they were never taught how to read the telltale signs. The signs appear both emotionally and physiologically as symptoms. Physical symptoms are the body's way of telling us when we are making harmful choices. Likewise, emotional symptoms communicate when we are harming our spiritual body. When we achieve a fluency in the language of symptoms and learn to pay attention to the conversation, we can use this dialogue to guide us through life. Until then, we'll continue to create and perpetuate all kinds of obstacles in our lives—especially those related to food!

The common but catastrophic approach to disease today is to look only at symptoms and proceed to tackle them one by one. First we give it a name, a diagnosis. Then we treat the diagnosed disease with a medication that contributes toxicity to the body and causes other symptoms, but we call it a cure because it relieves the original complaint. According to modern medicine, the majority of illnesses are more or less a mystery, and once a large enough percentage of the public experiences an illness, it is considered normal.

Yet, if we apply a bit of common sense, we can easily understand all diseases as manifestations of the same cause: obstruction in the organism due to inorganic substances and their by-products. How these obstructions manifest as symptoms is the only variable.

When an organism lives in opposition to life, or against its inherent nature, it attempts to self-destruct. In the same way that an autoimmune disease is an event of cells attacking one another, emotional eating is also a self-destructive action—it's an autoimmune disease of the emotional body that uses the physical body and food as vehicles of expression. In both cases, they are occurring because of unnatural living.

Whether emotional or physical, all disease, at its core, is caused by living in opposition to natural laws. "You cannot break the Law," one wise teacher emphasized. "You can only break yourself against the Law." This is precisely what most of us are doing today as we manifest myriad symptoms of deterioration. If we don't make life-generating choices, we cannot expect to radiate life-generating qualities. Yet, everywhere we turn, our culture demands that we somehow do both.

The autoimmune reaction of the body attacking itself is just an extreme symptom of living in opposition to natural laws. Today's extreme symptoms reflect the depth of physical and emotional poisoning over a long period of time—spanning not just decades, but generations upon generations of people poisoning their blood and cells with gluey, acidic substances.

The preponderance of widespread autoimmune diseases (and infertility, the ultimate indicator of a species' non-viability) that we are seeing today tells us that the offenses against nature have gone on for too long and have nested far too deeply for us to take lightly.

But are we listening? Do we understand the signs? When we consume substances that oppose the integrity of our cellular structure, we must expect undesirable physical and emotional experiences. Are we better off continuing to live in conflict with nature by taking more drugs and developing new symptoms?

Sure, we can continue to demand that our bodies and the natural world pretzel in Herculean maneuvers around these substances—and they will, but at a very steep price, until the substances simply break us. *Or* we can choose to consume substances that work in harmony with nature to raise us to our greatest physical and emotional potential.

Yes, of course, the latter is the preferable option. But then why are our "leaders" (governments, educators, corporate executives, medical and scientific institutes, and even some charities) either missing this obvious fact or deliberately ignoring it? I suspect that most of them are so programmed that they are blind to reality. The rest, meanwhile, are too driven by selfish, short-sighted personal agendas.

We don't need a particularly high IQ to figure out how we got into this hyper-diseased state of humanity. We just need to wake up. New diagnoses are always springing up, but they are just new names of commonly perceived imbalances. These names serve, above all, to drive fear and fundraisers.

Let's face it, no other species in the known history of the planet appears to have an overeating problem, much less need to be briefed on appropriate levels of consumption (i.e., numbers of meals, calories, nutrients, and so on). Until the civilization of our species, food consumption has only ever been instinctual and uncomplicated.

So why now? Why does our species need this kind of guidance now? Because we have lost touch with our intuition around food due to utterly unnatural living. Modern cultural wiring, corporate motives, and governmental agendas ignore the factors that have warped our natural instincts around food—instincts that have kept us surviving, evolving, and thriving for millions of years. Why? Such considerations would undermine the bovine herd mentality, which society's machinery relies on to lead the masses away from personal responsibility and straight into its furnaces.

Personal responsibility is anathema to corporate industry, which thrives on the mindless consumption of unnecessary, mass-produced products (everything from widgets to diet supplements to pharmaceuticals). In other words, the puppeteers of consumerism can only hold sway over toxic people in a toxic mindset. Clear, self-directed, aware individuals would easily see through the system and threaten its success.

What would happen if the blinders came off and everyone could see the truth about our society, its bureaucracy, and how its manipulations have kept us in a holding pattern of dissatisfaction and dependence? Would it shock us? I suspect we would be inspired to create a less self-serving and more whole-serving vision for human life. The old model would dissolve and in its place would develop the next stage of our evolution.

Illusions of wealth, success, happiness, and satisfaction would be revealed for their hollowness and would dissolve in short order. But then what? What would there be without the system's strongholds of social programming? There would be a burgeoning of creativity, individuality, and human connection, along with soaring levels of physical well-being and natural joy. Meanwhile, those who once benefited from the old system of greed and illusion, those who feared alternative ways of life, would be at a loss.

Of course, today's mainstream consumerism and the mainstream diet represent a gross deviation from our natural inclinations. Now is the time to reclaim the gift of our true physical, emotional, and spiritual natures—to rescue our precious lives from the paradigm of suffering. And the only way to do this is to educate ourselves away from the pitfalls of addiction, dissatisfaction, and limitation.

In Part I of this book, we will discuss how the false authorities of social conditioning have dramatically derailed us. In Part II, we will get to the root of self-destructive behavior through an inquiry into consciousness. In Part III, we will revive the spirit-body connection. Finally, in Part IV, we will lay out the essential steps and exercises for our journey back to balance and wholeness.

PART I

The False Authority
of Social Conditioning

What the "Authorities" Won't Tell Us

None of the government-funded research studies being done today will ever tell us about wellness. All these studies do is showcase the norms for people who are already in a state of decline.

Yet, the authorities use their credentials and god-like images to dress partial truths up to look like hard science and sell them to an unquestioning public. Images of doctors in lab coats at top universities connote advanced thinking and lend a well-established breed of credibility—a credibility that, while often warranted, is just as often completely unworthy of its power. In their position, the authorities can convince the public that they are using their highest scientific faculties and highest integrity, when often they are just grasping at straws.

I prefer to use the language of what we might call "common-sense science," which tells us that the human petri dish, once exposed to mainstream consumption, becomes a bacteria-laden cesspool rife with fermenting, putrefying matter. This creates all kinds of blockages, perpetuating all manner of physical and non-physical discomforts, poor health, and poor body image.

Nutrition sciences tabulate ideal caloric consumption and measure nutritional food values. This information is used formulaically for the individual in need of weight loss. Now, numerical and nutritional food values have their place; I'm not categorically dismissing their value. However, out of context, as they usually are, they do not serve people very well, particularly not emotional overeaters. Emotional eating and its complications (the by-products that ravage the system with yeast, causing further weight gain) are the main causes of weight problems.

If you are self-soothing with starches and creamy, sugary substances, merely knowing that these substances have too much sugar and fat will burden you with a sense of shame and guilt. This is the nature of addiction: to reach again and again for a quick fix, only to end up feeling physically and emotionally worse.

Awareness about food composition and nutritional value is indeed worthwhile, but it's not the place to begin if the problem is emotional eating. Textbook nutrition facts and diet programs are not going to solve the core issue. Diet talk is cheap in the presence of so much internal dissonance.

But then, of course, emotions themselves are so misunderstood and mishandled in today's world, as we will discuss further in Parts II and IV. The first step is to learn how to read our emotions and what they are telling us. When we understand our emotions, they can become a formidable ally, capable of directing us and freeing us from cycles of despair.

Once understood and applied, the emotional alarm bells will quiet down and return to their watchtower. Only from this position of power can an addict hope to be stronger than the addictive substance. If you're eating for emotional reasons, you're eating outside the context of purposeful consumption. Obviously, there are degrees to this. Almost everyone in what we call the civilized world uses food as an emotional crutch. If they are not using food, they are using cigarettes, alcohol, caffeine, or some other mood-stabilizing, addictive substances and escapist activities.

Calories, fat grams, portion sizes, and endless diet programs are constantly discussed in the media, in doctors' offices, and among friends and family. Meanwhile, it's emotional eating that really blocks people from implementing dietetic improvements. Emotional eating should be at the forefront of dietary discussions.

In my experience, attempting to make dietary changes without working out the emotional kinks is almost always a futile endeavor, an uphill battle all the way. But once you dissolve the self-sabotaging emotional roots of the problem, you will see how easy it is to implement useful changes!

Socially Conditioned Eating

In order to begin to understand emotional eating, we must discuss social conditioning, which was once a very little-known term but is becoming more widely used among today's conscious youth. Social conditioning refers to the norms that we have inherited practically from birth; they are so much a part of the fabric of our culture that it can feel strange to question them. But here's what we need to understand: these norms are intimately connected with the act of emotional eating.

Social conditioning at large has compromised our sanity, but socially conditioned *eating* specifically has given rise to all of our eating disorders—from relatively mild expressions to full-blown cases. If it were not for social conditioning, we would not have eating disorders. Only civilized people have eating disorders. But why is this so? In the answer to this question lies the solution for emotional eating.

Pondering this question in light of all my personal and professional experience, logic, and intuition has led me to the conclusion that our stresses, anxieties, regrets, primal childhood experiences, repressed emotions, and blocked creativity are all symptoms of our social wiring. Our way of life constricts us, limits us, and emotionally poisons us.

With all due respect to our society's merits, among them are some devastating drawbacks. I remain hopeful that we may become innovative enough to take the best of civilization and leave behind the rest—that which does not serve our evolving good.

In the meantime, though, the social blueprint that we are asked to accept renders us physically and emotionally handicapped. However, we are trained not to see this, so it does not often get discussed. This social blueprint does not make life more abundant, more harmonious, or more fertile. It does not create a more life-generating personal and communal experience. Nonetheless we are told to accept—or rather, swallow—it without question. When we do swallow it and it turns out to be a bitter pill that makes us physically and emotionally ill, we seldom attempt to challenge it.

It's an odd social phenomenon that most of us keep trying to make the pieces of the blueprint fit when, deep down, we know they never will. That's how people are wired. In the same way that children want to believe their parents are perfect, the citizens of a community are conditioned to believe that theirs is a working model—they *want* to believe in it. Moreover, they want to believe that their cultural model is the *only working model*. That, above all other models, theirs gets it right and is, to boot, governed by the most superior authorities in the history of humankind.

Products of the civilized world want to make the civilized world look like it works even when it doesn't. For all the various investments of time, education, and social posturing, they want to believe it's working. Further, many suffering souls secretly feel they are the only ones for whom the system isn't working, and thus believe something must be wrong with them.

Often by trying to make the social blueprint work, we wind up stuffing ourselves with food, because it has the remarkable effect of distracting us from our problems. The more we live in conflict with our true selves, the more we desire to disappear from the world we live in. We soon learn we can avoid these feelings of internal conflict by putting something really tasty in our mouths. Food becomes a portal to temporary escape—from all that feels wrong about our life experience.

So here we are with a situation where our socially conditioned lifestyle, particularly our mainstream diet, renders us emotionally hog-tied. We have set up causes and effects that keep us in cycles of suffering. In order to free ourselves of emotional eating, we must fully recognize that social conditioning has wired us according to its dictates. Only from this perception will we be able to dissolve distortions and illusions that have been bred into us throughout the course of many generations.

Social conditioning is a lens superimposed over all our cognitive faculties. It's a way of seeing that has been programmed into us from birth. But we are so conditioned to it that it does not appear distorted. It's kind of like a deep humming or droning that goes unnoticed until it is switched off, and only then is there awareness and a sigh of relief.

What is more important and fundamental to quality of life than deciding what to put and what not to put into our bodies? Yet, so often we are as oblivious to the social conditioning that directs our food choices as we are to the fact that our hearts are beating. We are like programmed robots, eating specified substances at specified times. Even if you think you are aware and making healthy choices, chances are you are making programmed choices. Even what is officially deemed healthy is a choice that has been made for you by social forces.

Most so-called health programs today promote a false sense of security by offering suggestions that sound good but simply do not result in health. These include mainstream dietary guidelines, supplementation, flu shots and other inoculations, rice cereal for babies, large quantities of animal proteins, grain starches, dairy, and water supplies contaminated with chlorine—all carrying myriad toxic chemicals deemed suitable for human consumption. These substances may not trigger immediate death or dysentery, but the accumulation of them over time will cause emotional imbalance, digestive distress, all manner of diseases, and premature death.

Millions of people adhere to strict gym workouts and diets prescribed by social health authorities, yet they continue to suffer and depend on addictive substances. They remain quietly perplexed, off balance, struggling with the food-body conundrum of our culture. Moreover, they are far quicker to blame themselves than the authorities. It's eerie, but the illusion, reinforced by each person who buys into it, makes it stronger than the truth.

Overeating is always the result of emotional eating. Imagine a set of Russian dolls: Emotional eating would be the outermost doll, the one shoveling food into her mouth. Inside that doll, you'll find the doll of socially conditioned eating. Inside that doll, you'll find the doll of social pressure. Inside that doll, you'll find the doll of subconscious pain, formed during childhood. Inside that doll is the doll of primal suffering, formed from a series of grievances against nature during the earliest stages of life. Inside that doll is the spirit, which is still alive but being smothered beneath so many layers of falsehood. She is right there at the center. This is the soul dying, the core pain.

Our true dietary home refers specifically to what the human body is biologically designed to consume—the nutrient-rich substances that it can readily metabolize and assimilate in order to derive optimal vitality. Then there is the category of largely deleterious substances that our culture has deemed appropriate for human consumption. So we have two radically conflicting dietary paradigms: the one fit for human life but generally ignored (if not ridiculed) by the public, and the culturally accepted norm that undermines human life.

Yet, we might be tempted to ask: *Wouldn't we be crazy to challenge all the published research data, all those popular programs and diets, all those new diagnoses and acronyms—and of course, who could forget, the FDA-approved food pyramids?* But this is precisely the blinkered mentality that has trapped the majority of us in a paradigm of suffering.

We celebrate what we call "civilized" by today's standards and dismiss the tremendous knowledge that we could glean from more "primitive" civilizations, if only we opened ourselves up to them. Tribal communities have much to teach us about creating and sustaining lives that work, but we continue to destroy them—and, along with them, the wisdom that has carried the torch for the human race for millions of years.

We are fiercely proud of our culture. We love having endless choices in our local supermarkets, in our car dealerships, in our malls—yet what have we sacrificed to have all those boxes of processed foods and irradiated fruits? What do we give up in community fellowship by living in isolated homes where mothers raise children in dire loneliness?

Is there another way—a way to embrace the unlimited creativity of the human spirit and exist in harmony with the world? Yes, I believe we have it in us to meet this lofty goal. Some intrepid souls are already forging new paths, and perhaps you will join the effort.

But first, we must understand that the paradigm of suffering that we've all inherited is fueled by greed, vanity, and power, and that most commercial products and socially rooted ideologies are not remotely for our highest good. We'd all like to believe that corporations and governments have our best interests in mind, but they do not! Even the honest few entities and individuals who have noble intentions are usually just as programmed and blind to the brokenness of their systems as the rest of the public. They only know how to perpetuate the problem, not fix it.

Food, Money, Image

Modern life is debilitating a growing majority of people with physical and emotional turmoil that's causing all kinds of bizarre behavior around food. But there must be a way to cultivate the highest expressions of civilization, of art and science and cultural fulfillment, without perpetuating all this senseless suffering.

Three key factors—food, money, and image—have become agents of corporate greed. All manner of chemically processed, toxic food products are manufactured, marketed, and sold for tremendous profit. Then, as if that weren't madness enough, mainstream consumers, unaware of where their food comes from or what havoc it wreaks on the body, constantly obsess about weight and physical appearance. A curious cycle indeed!

The idols of food, money, and image have transformed structurally poor but formerly benign nutritional ideas passed along from the last few centuries into the lethal norms around food consumption that we see today. Today's big food industry and the public's addiction to its unnatural products have devastated our health at every conceivable level!

Blindly following the authority figures has gotten us into this mess. Opening our eyes and determining truth from fiction is the only path that will get us out. The good news is that many of us are awakening to the scary realities of the mainstream diet, but then, so are the authorities. The problem is that they are not really trying to fix anything. Rather, they are merely cranking out countless variations of soy, dairy, animal protein, and grain products—and marketing them aggressively as "health foods."

Corporations, governments, and medical institutions have our trust. They have our business. They even have our gratitude! What do we have? Do we have the power of reflection? Can we ask the necessary questions? Are we afraid of offending someone if we do? Are we afraid we might look silly if we start living differently? Are we afraid of being wrong? The wizards of industry and commerce do a good job of making us fearful. But do their ideas make us well? Do their products and services prevent suffering or cause it? What is their motivation?

The authorities are getting away with systematic destruction. They are thriving while cases of autoimmune disease keep multiplying. We have reached the point where even the blind should be able to see what is happening. To not see it now is either to run from personal responsibility or to be too scared to face the truth. The fact is, taking personal responsibility for what you eat and how you live is much less scary than continuing along the path of self-destruction. The choice is always yours, but the desire to change has to come from within.

Human Food v. Industrial Food

Here's something you might not have expected: most of what we consume today is not even human food. Most people are shocked to learn that substances such as chicken, flour, cow milk, beans and soy beans—not to mention all the processed and packaged items made from these foods with chemical additives—are not even remotely fit for human consumption. That's right, the human body does not recognize these substances as health-generating foods.

Mindless consumption is the norm in our mainstream culture. And when we choose to eat something other than the absolute worst junk food, we give ourselves a big pat on the back. However, judging the value of foods relative to the most common denominator will never generate health in the human body. Quite the opposite.

Our bodies cannot adequately metabolize these mass-produced foods—including most of those deemed healthy by doctors, nutritionists, government health agencies, schools, and parents. They enter the body fully but they do not leave it fully. What happens when we put things in that do not go out? That's right, obstructions develop, creating material impediments to the proper flow and functioning of the body. All systems of the body, from intercellular communications to respiration, circulation, and digestion, become compromised.

A substance that cannot be broken down properly by an organism should not be placed in that organism. It will not provide sustenance. It is not health-generating, but health-deteriorating. This is common sense!

This does not mean that we are going to croak if we eat some of these things. Sure, we can snack on candy corn, Milk Duds, and sports bars; we can gulp down sodas and milkshakes; we can wolf down burgers, fries, and caramel popcorn. But just because it does not send us into anaphylactic shock upon swallowing does not mean it's human food.

Our bodies are incredibly adaptable; they are amazing at defending against foreign substances, at finding places to hold the excess residue from these foods. This is why the human species is still around. If we were so delicate that we disintegrated upon the ingestion of one harmful substance or another, we wouldn't have survived for this long as a species. However, just because it doesn't kill us upon consumption doesn't mean it's right for us, or that it won't accumulate, weigh us down, and kill us slowly over time.

What I call human food is fully metabolized by the body. It enters the alimentary canal, is digested, assimilated for necessary nutrients and energy, and then its residue is *fully eliminated*.

I say "Metabolization"/ You say "Metabolism"

Let's establish something fundamental about the "metabolism" that everyone talks so much about: There is not a single doctor in the world who can point to your metabolism. You don't have a metabolism per se. What you do have is a body comprised of cells, tissues, and organs that process substances. What the cells, the digestive system, and other vital organs support is what I prefer to call *metabolization*: the act of ingestion, absorption, assimilation, and elimination. Metabolization is an active process, not a static noun!

An intestinally and cellularly clean body can ingest human food seamlessly and fully, leaving nothing behind but energy. There are only a few categories of substances that offer this kind of seamless metabolization upon ingestion: namely, water-containing plant foods—meaning raw, unadulterated fruits and vegetables, young coconuts, and mother's milk for babies. That's it. All other foods, to varying degrees, leave waste behind in the body and are therefore impure human foods.

However, less pure foods still play an important role in a transitional diet. For example, fish, while not a purely human food, will leave less residue behind in the body than Milk Duds.

Fish is a biochemically organic substance comprised of water and amino acids that the body can recognize, whereas Milk Duds are caramel coloring, pasteurized dairy, refined sugar, and a whole bunch of other completely foreign substances that the body cannot compute.

So I am not saying that everything that is not a purely human food gets lumped into the same category. Of course not! There are many foods that, while not perfectly pure like water-containing fruits and veggies, are nevertheless safe to consume and, furthermore, given the current condition of our physiology, often recommended. (I explain the reasons for this in detail in my previous books.)

In order to free ourselves from the trap of social conditioning, and of emotional eating, we need to rediscover who we really are. Our social conditioning undermines the beauty and brilliance of our natural organic structure and reduces us to products of social ideologies that do not serve our short- or long-term viability.

We've seen this in the context of the physical body. Those of you who have read my previous books understand the logic behind detoxification. When waste and its by-products are festering inside your body, your system becomes a cesspool of yeast, carbonic gas, and putrefactive and fermenting debris. The body not only gains excess weight, but ultimately decomposes from within due to the chemical reactions and proliferation of these substances.

Under such conditions, the human organism cannot regenerate or remain as strong as it was designed to be. However, if we remove the harbingers of decomposition—voila!—we have a flawlessly functioning, clean, lean, and happy organism!

The Alternative to Social Conditioning

If you do not think the world is a beautiful place or that your life is not special, it's a sure sign that agents of mass hypnosis have corrupted aspects of your being. Once you detoxify, you will see the world and yourself as remarkable. So many people come to me hating their bodies and cursing their images in the mirror. But after a good deal of detoxing, their old corrupted bodies and mindsets melt away and their beautiful selves emerge—and they love it. Life is infinitely more beautiful in a clean body and a clear mind!

The process of physical, mental, and emotional detoxification frees us to be who we really are. If this discussion of social conditioning and detoxification rings true for you, this means you are still awake enough to know that the old, inherited programs are undermining you. Just feeling that inner nod is like having the wind at your back propelling you toward truth, which is all you need to begin the journey of recovery. However, consider yourself warned: the journey to releasing all that toxicity is far from smooth sailing!

Our world of suffering is not a natural expression of human life, but rather a serious aberration of modernity. Our society spits out suffering like baseballs from a pitching machine in a batting cage—faster and more brutally than we can handle. We are spinning in cycles of sickness, debt, depression, loneliness, psychosis, and countless forms of physical and social pain. Yet, our defective social system is continually reinforced with each new elected official, each purchase of artificial food, each parent who raises his or her child in front of the TV screen.

Many well-intentioned individuals come along and try to introduce new and better programs. If you think about it, the many social revolutions we've seen throughout history were attempts at remedying a dysfunctional blueprint. But none of them have worked, so I'm not suggesting that we need anarchy or revolution.

What we need is evolution. We need a new vision of wholeness. Interconnectedness is what makes every organism thrive—whether we're talking about a body, a garden, or a rainforest. All healthy systems thrive on interdependence, with all parts serving the whole. We cannot achieve this with another toxic program or another pill. We need to ask ourselves: *How did things get this way? What do we need to change in order to make the body whole and sustainable again?*

Anything short of a vision rooted in wholeness, in regenerating functionality for the entire system, is shortsighted. But it requires mavericks who are willing to pull back the curtain on all the rubbish that has been shoved aside. And what better place to begin than with ourselves?

How many of us follow the path of least resistance to jobs we hate, to meals that sicken us, to relationships that reinforce our toxic lifestyles, to popular messages that keep us feeling inferior in every way? Social conditioning creates a daily experience that renders us dissatisfied, yet for various reasons we surrender to and cannot see past it.

Exercise: How Socially Conditioned Are You?

If you haven't already done so, sit with this concept of social conditioning for a few days or weeks, witnessing your life patterns, your family, your friends, your job, the media, and your larger community to see just how programmed we all are. At first you might resist and resent what you see, especially if you take social mores very seriously and have invested a great deal in labels, titles, status, and wealth at the expense of personal responsibility and fulfillment.

Allow yourself to feel the shock of recognition, sit with your discoveries for as long as you need to and question them as much as you like. But then follow your intuition. If you let it, your intuition will lead you to your more liberated, empowered self. Among other things, it will help you to overcome the scourge of emotional eating.

It may take you a few weeks or a few months before you can move forward. While it's true that in the eleventh hour it would behoove us all to awaken and fix things rapidly, we cannot force it—that would only make us backfire. The power of awakening to our social conditionings must come from within, not from some outside pressure or trend.

Now that we understand social conditioning, we can see its role in our eating patterns. The voices of our doctors, teachers, parents, newscasters, advertisers, and countless other authorities have cemented into us an ideology around food—what to eat, what's considered healthy, what's considered desirable, what to eat socially, what to snack on after school, what to eat when studying for finals, what to eat when watching a ball game, when gathering for the holidays, when nursing a broken heart, when on an airplane, on a date, in a theater. Society has also taught us exactly what time to eat our meals, what to drink with them, and even which supplements and super-foods to add.

But that's not all. Society has also told us how much to eat, how much is too much—all while pressing on us heaps of the most processed, acidic, addictive substances known to humankind. Then, to add insult to injury, society has told us exactly how we should look, holding us to standards of beauty that we could not possibly achieve on this diet.

My friends, no other species in history eats according to a clock or from a package, or chooses their food based on the numbers on a label or the persuasive powers of a commercial. Can you imagine a bunch of bunnies huddled around a TV screen determining what to eat after watching an ad for Mr. McGregor's carrot chips—or buying into the olestra version? Yes, in our culture, we'd rather consume indigestible fats and have gas and diarrhea than go without our potato chips! Olestra is right up there with saccharine, margarine, and fat-free milk products—marketed as healthful to the addicted, hypnotized masses. *This is your brain on social conditioning!*

So here we are, laden with a whole system of cemented lies and illusions. It's time to dismantle and toss out nearly everything we've been told about how to eat and care for the body, even if it means being ridiculed or rejected by the herd. Of course, this is not necessarily a very inviting option—even for the renegade nonconformist. I fully empathize with this dilemma. I've been there myself.

If you're up for the challenge, however, you'll soon find that all that intimidation from mainstream society is just smoke and mirrors. Yes, you'll get some grief from the tribe, but it will die down once they know you're serious and they see your life dramatically improving. Once your tribe picks up on your joy and liberation, they'll start huddling around you for the right reasons, and you'll find yourself smack dab on the right side of change.

This concludes our focus on social conditioning. Let us now look more closely at its inevitable offspring: self-destructive behavior.

PART II

Getting to the Root of Self-Destructive Behavior

It's a Mad World After All

That's what we have, a social organization that works beautifully for products—which just keep getting better and better every year—but very poorly for people, except for the greedy, the ruthless, and the power hungry.

- Daniel Quinn

Daniel Quinn says it best: We have built a civilization that works great for cars, cell phones, and guns, but it just doesn't work for people. Our self-destructive behaviors signal that this world is not working for us. Our inner madness mirrors our cultural madness.

We often forget that our emotions relay information to us about how the inner self is responding to the external environment. In the words of the great modern mystic Almine, *anger* is the desire to protect; *pain* is the desire to change; and *joy* is the desire to live. Pain and anger are central to self-destructive behaviors such as emotional overeating and substance abuse. Joy, in the presence of so much increasing pain and anger, is becoming scarce.

Pain and anger sound their alarms, signaling the need for protection and change against an outside threat. But what is the threat? It is a world that endangers the viability of life. If you are engaging in self-destructive behaviors, mild or severe, chances are your inner being has been calling out for protection and change via physical and emotional symptoms for some time, but your conscious mind hasn't known how to interpret them.

By the time you are fully engaging in self-destructive habits, you have stopped holding out hope for aid. You have hit the eject button on life—a life that, no matter how you try to make it fit, just doesn't.

If that sounds to you like an elongated suicide, you are hearing me correctly! In order to arrest this subconscious death cycle, we must first understand it. We need to see why our civilization doesn't work for humans (or for any life form) and what exactly needs to change. We also need to know how to cope with a compromised situation in the meantime.

How Long Have You Been Sleeping?

You might not have thought much about it before, but you have a particular worldview. You see the world from a certain perspective that shapes what you think and feel about everything around you. Lying at the root of most self-destructive behavior is a worldview that's as distorted and dangerous as it is widely accepted.

Our civilization espouses ideologies that run in direct opposition to life. Some ideas and actions generate and sustain life, whereas others destroy it. Our civilization suffers from a form of madness: it assumes the virtue of desecrating the life cycle in the name of commercial expansion, progress, health, safety, and entertainment—in short, "the good life." This assumption is so ingrained in the common consciousness that it's hardly ever questioned. Yet, your higher intelligence recognizes this as a threat to you and your world.

All too often we treat ourselves just as we do other living resources: *as a means to an end.* Just as we are stripping the land and water of life through deforestation, mining, drilling, and overfishing, we are sacrificing our own bodies and minds to the impossible demands of our culture. We are becoming overweight, underweight, and infertile as rogue microbes are exterminating trillions of life-generating microbes.

It took a lot of compromised life experience for me to recognize that my worldview was destroying the planet and myself. But once I did, I understood that self-destructive behavior signals a toxic relationship between oneself and one's environment.

A mad, mad world creates a mad, mad individual, and vice versa. It's a vicious cycle. Our bodies and minds reflect our communal perspectives and the values and actions that stem from them. We could no more recover from self-destructive behavior ignoring this phenomenon than an orange could grow detached from an orange tree. Our self-destructive behaviors are symptoms of a larger madness. They reveal the non-viability of our culture.

In my practice and through extensive work with a diverse population, I have come to realize that the vast majority of people are suffering from self-destructive behavior—and often in the form of over-consumption. Some people are better than others at hiding it, but it's ultimately a pandemic. Those who are not overeating are taking pills, drinking excessively, having affairs, over-exercising, or taking their madness out on their loved ones.

If trapped in the body, imbalanced emotional energy stagnates and causes the individual to become sick on many levels. When you look around at all the showered, coiffed, and crisply attired people striding down the street, don't assume that they've got it all together. In modern life, we tend to bury ourselves beneath layers of social pretense to conform to a worldview that neglects our true selves. This is not how life has to be. But before we change, we must understand that civilization is in many ways incompatible with our humanity. The norm today is to live in self-denial.

We are being destroyed by the very culture we unconsciously buy into wholesale. It appears to be the only choice we have, so we try to adjust and carry on. But no matter how hard we try, we can never fully adjust to a system that serves industry and products over human life, so we suffer. We suffer and stuff, drug, and drink ourselves into temporary numbness until we need our next dose.

Into the furnaces of mass production and consumption (the pillars of our society) we march, and we wonder why it hurts, why we keep doing the crazy things we do. There must be something wrong with us, we conclude.

If you fear that you cannot cope with the world as it is, that you'll never fit in, you are not alone. Do not assume anything is wrong with you. In fact, it is likely a sign that your inner spirit is still alive and kicking, rebelling against a mad, mad world. If you understand the origins of the madness and self-destructive behavior, you will be able to take back the reins of your life. It all starts with pulling back the layers of what we are *programmed to see* to reveal what *actually is*. This is called increasing your perception, expanding your consciousness. Stay with me as we go for a little ride through consciousness and our civilization.

In Part I, we pulled the curtain back on the misguided cultural perceptions of what constitutes a healthy, balanced diet. Through our cultural lens, we would consume substances that make no sense for us to consume—that have such life-deteriorating effects, it's a wonder any intelligent group would ever adopt them. Have you noticed how liberating it is to see something you couldn't see before? What you uncover dissolves the weight of confusion, the burden of rules. Learning that the majority of foods common to the modern diet are not even foods that your cells can process solves a lot of puzzles. Such is the gateway to freedom: knowledge that removes burdens, fears, and pains. That kind of knowledge, if we know what to do with it, is power.

But not all knowledge is power. Most knowledge is just information, some useful, some not so useful. Our brains amass information over the course of a lifetime—facts and observations learned in school, on the job, through daily experience—but it's not all necessarily empowering.

For too long, we have been asleep at the helm, letting commercial forces pull us along like riptides into the rocks of our self-destructive behaviors. We need to wake up. We need to tap into the kind of knowledge that unites with our consciousness, that becomes our life's navigation system, shapes our worldview, and steers our life choices.

Understanding the Life Cycle

All living things come into being through the life cycle: energy is birthed into an organism that blossoms and then decomposes. Then that energy, upon completed decomposition (death of the matter), can be recycled into another energetic form. Energy is neither created nor destroyed, just recycled.

The decomposition cycle is initiated when an organism perceives itself or its environment to be non-viable. The organism's higher intelligence begins the process automatically, preferring the release of decomposition to the effort of generating and sustaining life force in a sick environment. In today's culture, self-abusers—including emotional eaters—have no shortage of substances to choose from to accelerate their own decomposition.

In theory, you could easily preempt this decomposition cycle by insisting upon a life-generating environment. But even at later stages of self-destructive behavior, you can use this knowledge to identify what triggered the cycle and start making corrections to your environment.

If your capacity for change is limited at the moment, you can empower yourself simply by observing what generates life and what does not. From there, you can discern between the madness that resides within you and the madness that lies outside of you. There will always be some disturbances to your harmony, but at least you'll be aware of what's triggering the chaos. Even when you're in the eye of the storm, you can stop denying yourself and pretending your environment works.

To recap, the two parts of the life cycle are: (1) the generating cycle where life evolves and blossoms and (2) the degenerating cycle where the energy infused into living things waits while the physical vessel decomposes. Upon the end of the latter cycle, the energy that animated the organism ultimately leaves the physical vessel for recycling. This phenomenon applies to every aspect of life. As long as you keep this in mind, whenever something's going wrong, you can usually cut right to the solution.

Now, in light of what we know about the cycles of life and decomposition, we can delve into the question of consciousness.

Consciousness: Getting to Know You...

What is *consciousness*, really? The term is tossed around so casually today that is has become nearly stripped of its meaning and widely misunderstood. The term is overused as a catchall for anything that falls under the eco-, green, new-agey, yoga, Eastern religion umbrella. But consciousness is a very real and powerful tool that deserves our greatest care and respect.

In the most concise terms, consciousness is the union of self-awareness and environment-awareness. Consciousness is the most fundamental aspect of our experience as human beings. The extent to which we are aware of ourselves and our environment is the extent to which we are present, human, alive—*right now, right here, on this planet!*

Some people are aware of very little. They see what they are programmed to see and hardly know themselves at all. Others are highly self-aware, always observing and evaluating their own thoughts and behaviors as well as their responses to others and to their situations. We all operate at different levels of awareness, and we all have the ability to increase our awareness.

Cultivating consciousness can save lives and create new lives. It can alleviate pain and prevent future pain. It can strengthen communication and human connection, and thus make life worth living. Take, for example, the mother-and-child relationship. If every mother in the world caught her behavior when she began to take her stress out on her child, which could easily trigger a lifetime of emotional imbalance, she would ideally stop that behavior, or at the very least acknowledge the affront and apologize for it before it could do further damage.

When you increase your consciousness, it's like opening your eyes for the first time: you see things that you absolutely did not see before. You could no more go back to your old way of seeing as you could unlearn how to ride a bicycle. The impact of this awareness on your life is directly proportional to how greatly it's increased. Best of all, consciousness leads to greater insights that lead to greater consciousness: it's a never-ending thrill ride!

Your consciousness is your navigation system through life—it is the best GPS you'll ever have! If you're not careful, subliminal and not-so-subliminal cultural messages will cause interference and throw you off course. But the more you exercise and heighten consciousness, the better you'll become at navigating the confusing terrain of modern life.

Exercise: Tune Into Your Consciousness

Consider your degree of awareness for a moment. Just tune into what your conscious mind is taking in and then notice what it has not noticed until this moment. Increased consciousness leads to increased perception. Imagine that I've placed you in a world of reds and greens and then removed the filters that prevented you from seeing the blues, yellows, purples, and oranges. Only, in this case, there are no material filters—just your conscious mind taking in more of the environment. Now, take a moment to review and answer these questions: What is consciousness? What does it feel like to increase consciousness? What are the perimeters of your awareness? What might you see beyond them with increased consciousness?

It wasn't until my own alarm bells began ringing very loudly that I finally became conscious of their message and sought to protect my life—to make changes that would stop the pain. After two decades of school, I set out for an education of a different sort: a self-education that would either set me free of the pain and protect my being from future harm or confirm that the world wasn't a viable place for me.

Over the course of my self-education, I started to see things that explained why the world seemed so full of madness and nonsense to me. Today, I can freely say that if I had not actively expanded my consciousness and cultivated self-awareness in order to solve many of the riddles of my life, I would have ended my life by now. Until then, society felt like a torture chamber with no escape hatch.

What especially helped me to understand why this modern way of life felt so broken was learning about two different types of consciousness. The first is called "unity consciousness," the way organisms live and thrive together in nature. The second is "separation consciousness," the way our world is dying, with the life of each organism being snipped off at its source. I hope these two models and their principles help you take a great big leap in understanding as they did for me.

Unity Consciousness

Unity consciousness assumes that there is one massive consciousness, sometimes referred to as "the one life." It has a spirit and form that contains individuated consciousnesses. These individuated lives coexist in a state of interdependence. The viability of the individual lives are dynamically interlinked. Each organism is affected by the viability and health of all the other organisms within the larger whole. From this perspective, every single organism (single-celled or trillion-celled) has a purpose, and the well-being of each individuated organism is relevant to the well-being of the whole, and vise versa.

Imagine the Earth as one massive organism and all the smaller organisms that live on and within it are interconnected; corporately they comprise "the one life." Like members of a family, each smaller ogranism has a unique purpose that supports the whole. It is in the best interest of each to honor the function and existence of the others.

If we pull out on a larger scale, we can envision the Earth as an individuated consciousness within the whole organism of the solar system, which, to pull out on an even larger scale, is an individuated consciousness within the whole universe, and so on.

If we move in on the microcosmic level, we can envision the role of the cells of our bodies within the framework of the larger organism; the cells likewise rely upon the joining of viable, healthy atoms and molecules—the foundation of the cells which combine to form and support tissues, which combine to form and support organs, which combine to form and support the whole human body.

This concept is intrinsic to all life. Of course, this is a simplified explanation of how organisms work within and among other organisms, but it's the great web of unity consciousness. Joining the many organisms within "the one life" is a web, a great network that connects all life within the organism, both physically and non-physically. Life force energy flows through this network, which, if you could see it, would look like a spiderweb of conductors constantly transmitting information and essential elements between the smaller individuated consciousnesses, much as the branches of neurons and synapses in the brain connect to the nerves that run through the body, or as the roots of a forest of trees send and receive information back and forth seamlessly.

Vital physical elements such as water, blood, and electrons, as well as vital non-physical elements such as emotions and thoughts, are all conducted through this web.

Separation Consciousness

Now we have what I call "separation consciousness," whereby life is perceived to be made up of components, some original elements (such as oxygen and hydrogen) and others evolved (such as complex life forms). Separation consciousness views the world as a mechanistic, material machine, a concept that has become known as "reductionism." Whether we are talking about the human body or the solar system, adherents of separation consciousness take living things at material face value. They see what occurs under the microscope, through the telescope, and through the eyes. They believe only what they can see.

René Descartes, considered to be among the founders of modern science, argued that the world was like a machine, a clockwork mechanism that could be understood by taking its pieces apart, studying them, and then putting them back together again to see the larger picture. All life sciences and physical sciences are subject to separation consciousness. If there does not seem to be a more dynamic connection at face value, and it cannot be proven, then the concept is rejected.

Understanding the world through its components leads to their categorization. Categorization follows a hierarchical model. Let's take the human body, for example: some organs are more important (think: heart and lungs) while others are less so (think: thyroid and pancreas), and others are disposable (think: tonsils and appendix). Again, the hierarchy: important, less important, disposable.

The components need to be maintained if they are to survive. The more important ones dominate over the less important ones. Separation consciousness identifies structures in all aspects of its functioning along these hierarchical lines. Because separation consciousness is reductionist by nature, it asserts hierarchies everywhere. The basic structure designates a primary intelligence to govern over the smaller parts. Everything working properly according to its designated function requires hierarchies and controls. This is necessary at every level of engagement in separation consciousness. Otherwise, the mechanism would malfunction.

The world of separation consciousness is run like a factory with charges in place to execute and oversee all the various mechanics of life. In this model, everyone has a job, and the job is mandated, rigid, to be executed in isolation, not experienced or enjoyed. If you fail on the job, you will be fired.

Unlike unity consciousnesses, a model that receives life's necessities as naturally interlinking parts of a whole organism, separation consciousness requires life's necessities to be mined and extracted to serve the individual parts. Intrinsic to the separation model is that everyone is separate and responsible for oneself.

This perspective also has a non-physical component. Adherents of separation consciousness acknowledge the existence of non-physical aspects of life, but address them separately from the physical aspects. Sometimes, due to principles of cause and effect, they perceive the non-physical and the physical to overlap. For example, if a small child is hyperactive, they might ask what the child ate to cause that reaction. This, however, demonstrates a very limited sense of interconnectivity.

Reclaim Your Self-Worth

What if I told you that the vast majority of us move through life and make choices every day through the lens of separation consciousness? Then what if I told you that not everyone on this planet sees the world this way, that it's not a human phenomenon but a cultural one?

Separation consciousness is the root of our civilization as we know it. However, just because it has been the accepted way of seeing for the past ten thousand years doesn't mean it cannot be replaced by something better. Separation consciousness has conquered almost every square inch of life on this planet—human, animal, and plant—but it is just one way of seeing the world.

Unity consciousness offers a far more sustainable, life-generating way. Even in purely scientific, objective terms, when all parts of an organism work cooperatively, they sustain and regenerate each other. Separation consciousness, by contrast, is life-deteriorating: when individuated consciousnesses work for the good of their own separate selves, without regard for the whole, it affects the whole like a cancer, like an autoimmune disease.

We've all been drinking the same Kool-Aid, and now we are prisoners of our own separation consciousness. Like a nation of individual despots, we deem some aspects of life disposable and others not, choosing industry over sustainability, quantity over quality, surface beauty over inner health.

So we live alone in our isolated spaces with thyroid disorders. I'll take the trees and wild turkeys, thanks. We needn't strain too hard to see that everything has become a commodity. Our perception of "the good life" and of what's valuable has turned every single thing the civilized world touches—trees, land, water, animals, people—into a means to a very shortsighted end. Our society is a hierarchical system on steroids. While everyone has been focused on his or her own little myopic life, the juggernaut of separation consciousness has reached maturity. The entire planet has been divided: necessary, less necessary, disposable. And while no one was looking, the disposable list has grown astonishingly long.

Not all of the "disposables" are obvious. It's not just the trees and the land and the natives. You, too, are disposable. If you are a means to a corporation's end or to a government's end, you are disposable! Even if you aren't conscious of it, deep down you feel it. A new slave class has emerged. We are so disconnected from the whole that our values have become inhumane, but we are so blind that we haven't even noticed it.

You could name any of a dozen reasons that send people into emotional eating overdrive (stress, escapism, addiction, habit, numbing, moodiness, depression, emptiness, loneliness, isolation, social pressure, childhood trauma, and so on), but those are just symptoms of a mad, mad world. We cannot fix these things by looking at them one by one. We'd never get anywhere.

We have to go straight to the source of self-destructive behavior: our civilization is incompatible with life—not just human life, *all* life. We cannot be whole if we are destroying parts of ourselves. We are interconnected and highly functioning only when we act out of the values of interconnectedness. We cannot go around taking scissors to the web and not expect everything to die!

The ailing soul in an ailing environment turns to overeating and substance abuse to aid swift decomposition. To turn this cycle around and stop the subconscious suicide is a two-part effort: it requires (1) acknowledging that the civilized world is stuck in a life-destroying paradigm (separation consciousness); and (2) embracing a life-generating paradigm (unity consciousness).

Life, by its very definition, exists by the interconnected activities of energetically charged parts supporting each other. We must return to this fundamental truth if we wish to save ourselves from certain ruin. Until the madness of our world subsides and we start to see regeneration, we can use this knowledge to cultivate life-generating bodies and behaviors. It is not the perfect scenario, but it will gradually empower us and those whose lives we touch during the course of our journey.

Make no mistake, deep down you know that all the hierarchical corporations and governing bodies that steer our society perceive you as a disposable commodity. To accept a worldview that supports them is to devalue yourself. But how can you love yourself if you don't think you are worthy of living? *How can you feel connected in a disconnected world?* Ah ha, now we're onto something.

To value your own life is to value *all* life. It requires the will to live both consciously and subconsciously, to disavow the worldview of separation consciousness and reconnect the threads of unity consciousness. It is time we learn to love ourselves, down to our very cells, to feel the currents of energy we are always emitting and receiving from the world around us. From this worldview of unity consciousness, we can begin to honor ourselves and experience the fullness of life—physically, emotionally, spiritually. By drawing nourishment from our environment in this way, we can let the compulsions to stuff, purge, numb, and otherwise abuse ourselves naturally ebb away.

Yes, we live in a mad, mad world of isolation, miscommunication, and self-destructive behavior, full of people asleep at the helm. But it is within our power to wake up, reconnect, and reclaim our minds and bodies—and,

ultimately, our joy.

PART III

Reclaiming the Spirit-Body
Connection

What Is the Spirit?

The spirit and the body are designed to function as an interdependent team. They are actively connected, and this finely tuned dynamic must be maintained at all costs, lest the entire human organism collapse in ruin. Due to the mainstream lifestyle and our culture's profoundly warped concept of health and good living, most people today have a gravely compromised, low-functioning spirit. Moreover, most people in the modern world don't know what the spirit is, or that they even have one. Or else they completely dismiss the concept of spirit as some kind of primitive hocus-pocus, since it cannot be measured by hard science. The result: spiritual impoverishment, which is directly connected to physical impoverishment.

The spirit is what we commonly think of as "I"—the presence of one's true identity, which resides within, but is distinct from, the physical body. It has been referred to as the observer, or the Atman (the Hindu term referring to the macrocosmic soul or universal diety; or atman with a lowercase "a" referring to the microcosmic, individuated soul).

The spirit gathers information through the senses and the experiences of the body. The spirit is the active, living consciousness that directs the whole being. It is the experiencer-observer-director, the self that processes and makes determinations based on its experiences. Another way of describing this soul-spirit-self (which I will henceforth refer to simply as the spirit) is the unified force field of intelligence that is the true captain of each of us.

The human spirit is not a vague, indefinable, or esoteric concept. It is an unmistakable aspect of our humanity, and it's of the highest importance. Recognizing and honoring the spirit is essential to understanding the full anatomy of the human being. It is the only sure way to illuminate the full dimensions of what you are and how you are designed to function, so you can make the most of your time here on earth.

If you continue to struggle to grasp the meaning or accept the reality of the spirit, I urge you to take the time to meditate further on your true identity. Ask yourself the following questions:

- To whom or what am I referring every time I say "I" or "me" or "myself" in everyday conversation?

- Am I merely the sum of my physical parts (my brain, my arms, my legs, etc.)—no more and no less than my physical body—or is there something more to who I am?

- Am I simply a vessel of matter, interchangeable with any other human vessel with my precise chemistry, measurements, and levels of exposure to outside elements, or do my perceptions and sensory experiences contribute vitally and uniquely to who I am?

Despite the roots of religion running deeply throughout human history, we are culturally inept at conceptualizing the unseen. The spiritual is shrouded in mystery, a domain typically relegated to priests and theologians. In my personal experience—educated from birth in the dominant religion of the West, Christianity—I feel my religious instruction left me with less, not more, clarity about spirituality. I now suspect this is because my rigorous religious training fostered a belief that the spiritual was something outside of me, something that would hear me in prayer, and embrace (or disown) me in death, but was always a world away.

The impressions I received put walls between me and what I now clearly recognize as my spirit. I had to work hard for many years of my adult life to dissolve those walls. In hindsight, I can see how my early religious training convoluted for me the ultimate simplicity of spirit. If you have only learned about a great, powerful spirit outside of yourself, it may help to shift your concept of spirit to that powerful force that directs you from within.

Here, however, is not the place to tease out all the nuanced, philosophical implications of spirituality at large. What's important in the context of emotional eating is that you recognize within you this powerful force of intelligence that, if set free, can direct your life brilliantly. To live unaware of this is to miss the whole point of our humanity, and to put your whole self at risk.

Your spirit is the epicenter of your awareness, the captain of your whole being. Failing to recognize, respect, and protect it—as is customary in our world—is irrational and self-destructive. We live in an overwhelmingly mechanistic culture that values the mechanistic. It discards that which it cannot see or define according to its contexts (quantum physics, however, is holding ever-increasing sway in the field of science, and thus expanding people's appreciation of the "unseen sciences"). Plenty of other civilizations have grasped far more mind-bending concepts. Our society—with all its rules, conditions, and soul-killing domestication—rejects all that falls outside of its rigid structure as categorically non-credible.

Yes, there are great mysteries in the universe, but the role of the spirit as the center point of intelligence is not one of them. The existence of the human spirit seems a mystery to our culture because our culture emphasizes quantifiable material reality above all else. Educational institutions limit their curricula to subjects that *reflect* the functioning of our society, so that we can be "successful" within the existing framework. Education in our culture does not concern itself with matters of life on a larger scale. Instead of expanding our minds to embrace the full spectrum and interconnectedness of life and sentient experience, it restricts our consciousness to fit within carefully circumscribed subjects.

The brain alone is commonly mistaken as the sole center of intelligence. This is because the spirit, by contrast, is intangible, invisible, immeasurable, untamable, and scientifically unproven. But the functioning of the brain is not an end unto itself. Rather, it captures and relays information as a conduit for the spirit.

All our mainstream practices and choices draw on the computer brain. We hardly ever utilize our instincts or intuitions anymore. We are chronically "thinking"—that is, being told what to think, executing those thoughts, and worrying about the next thing to think about. We can easily spend a whole lifetime in a hive of incessant, reflexive thinking. The problem is that so much of what we think is just preprogrammed cultural stories, norms, and expectations—set up to feed us straight into the social structure of material consumption. We have already explored at some length the implications of programmed thinking, but for our purposes here, let us consider this: *the extent to which we've prioritized precisely the wrong kind of intelligence.*

From generations of suppression and neglect, the spirit of the modern individual has grown agitated and rogue—like a wild animal pacing in a cage. Or better yet, imagine a ship captain bound and gagged in the rear of the hull, forced to let his ship be directed by his computer. The captain watches, helpless, as his ship heads straight for stormy seas. His crew scatters into chaos, the mast collapses, and the wheel spins out of control, leading the vessel toward a disastrous end. Frustration causes the captain's blood to boil, fury courses through his veins—and all the while the programmed computer, emotionless, continues to calculate and recalculate the route without the wisdom of experience or the benefit of instinct. *This is your spirit suppressed!*

The human spirit doesn't sit bound and gagged for long. The welling frustration will seek out and leak into cracks and vulnerabilities. It will spill over into the workings of the individual's inner and outer life in ways that are not always visible—through, for example, binge eating or becoming intensely controlling about external circumstances in an attempt to stave off a mounting inner panic.

The least explosive way for the individual to release some of that rising pressure is to direct that discontent inward. After all, haven't we all been taught from birth *not* to scream or punch or throw a tantrum or, heaven forbid, say what we *really* think and feel? It has been drilled into us again and again that the worst thing we can possibly do is show our vulnerability. Sadly enough, it just so happens that the human being can remain in a state of denial for a very long time.

Sooner or later, however, the spirit will thrash against its shackles more and more violently, in increasingly painful emotional and physical expressions, until one of two things happens: the spirit is finally heard and given free expression, or it is ignored to the point of self-destruction.

The Body as Probe

The human spirit expresses itself through the body on a moment-to-moment basis through the full range of physical senses—including (but not limited to) hearing, touch, sight, smell, taste, breathing, balance, movement, pleasure, and pain. Through the physical body, the spirit (the "I" or the observer) can experience and interpret all aspects of the physical world.

The spirit's interpreted experiences are then communicated back to the physical body via neurological pathways and chemical responses, which transmit the physical and emotional experience to the DNA in a form it can decipher. The DNA then updates the being with what it receives in a process called adaptation. In a healthy, functional human, there is a constant flow of information between the spirit and the body/DNA; both spirit and body benefit as they mutually evolve via this exchange.

It might help to imagine the spirit as the observer inside a probe, the body. The better the communication between spirit and body, the more effective a probe the body can be for the spirit. This is a dynamic, interdependent relationship, central to our whole earthly experience!

The indwelling force field of intelligence grows by uncovering new knowledge (i.e., making the unknown known). The better equipped its probe, the deeper the spirit can venture into the physical world. In this way, the physical body is the spirit's gateway to growth. It is the way *you*—the indwelling epicenter of awareness—grow. If you really think about it, this is incredibly exciting! We all want to know what we are doing here on earth, in a body, privy to so much experience. Well, here is a big part of the answer: you are here to learn all that you can possibly learn, physically and spiritually, about the world of form, and thereby expand your being.

We are what we know. So the more we learn, the stronger we grow. The more experienced we become, the more we can understand and fulfill our human potential. What could possibly be more gratifying than to grow, to overcome, to demystify the great puzzles of our existence—and then be given the opportunity to express that growth in our everyday lives?

For example, only by physically exploring the African savanna or finding your way around a large urban capital will you gain first-hand knowledge of those worlds. Only by surviving the dangers of an environment—be it a snake bite in the wilderness or a mugging in the city—will you become truly aware of those dangers. By the same token, only by experiencing the unique thrills of any given environment will you truly come to appreciate them. This is not to say that you should recklessly seek out danger (life often has a way of bringing such experiences to you), but it is to say that if you always strive to be receptive to experience, *to pay attention*, you will reach ever-greater levels of spiritual wisdom. And once you've gained a masterful understanding of one environment, your spirit will naturally move you toward a new one, so that it may continually experience and grow and connect the dots.

When I am presented with a serious situation, I like to repeat this mantra to myself: "I am big enough for this." To me, this means that I have had enough experience plunging the depths of life that I can handle this situation; and if I use what I know, I can bring it to its highest expression. For example, because I have had my own struggles with emotional eating and addiction, I am spiritually big enough for it. I have excavated the problem for myself, and now I can help illuminate it for others. I am also big enough to navigate petty disagreements, dramas, and emotional breakdowns that people have right in front of me. Having lost a loved one, I am big enough to understand such sorrow and the phases of grief.

Having been exposed to violence and abuse, I know that territory well. The darker the territory you find yourself in, the more you see and the less you have to fear because you're already well acquainted with those frightening places. It's like solving a crime. You demystify the whole situation. From my experiences I now know the motivations and wounds of such perpetrators as well as what the victim will require to rise out of victimhood (and why they may choose not to). I own those experiences and the insights I gained from them. I can use those insights whenever I need to call upon them. Because I've been there and achieved an understanding of such experiences, they have no power over me. I have probed and expanded and gained a working mastery of them. Now, when I face a challenge, it's a new kind of challenge. People can spend their whole lives in Drama 101 or Introduction to Abuse, but I have worked hard to advance to higher learning.

If I encounter a daunting situation that is entirely new to me, I can say to myself, "Don't worry, Natalia, once you understand this, your spirit will be big enough for it. This experience is a kind of gift." If I did not consciously rise to the challenge before me, I would be doomed to suffer the same situation again and again. Encountering challenges can be a sign of growth, since a thriving spirit naturally gravitates toward new experiences and new challenges. As long as you're paying attention and working to expand your knowledge base, you need not fall into the rut of facing the same type of challenge again and again. Experiences, both pleasant and unpleasant, are opportunities to expand who you are.

Therefore, the suppression of spirit is the opposite of progress. In fact, it poses a dire threat to human life—indeed, to all life. This reminds me of a great bit of dialogue in the movie, *A Few Good Men*. When idealistic lawyer Daniel Kaffee demands of Col. Jessup, "I want the truth!" the colonel replies, "You want the truth? You can't handle the truth!" The irony is that in a world of so much inner pain and suppressed spirit, no one can handle the truth. No one wants to hear the solutions.

In fact, the socially contrived parameters of what can and cannot be expressed stand all around us like invisible electric fencing for domesticated animals. The moment you venture beyond them, you get a little "shock"—that's society letting you know by raising its proverbial eyebrow—so that you'll learn the rules and stay within the boundaries.

How much do we as a society want to bring an end to cancer, addiction, suicide, and countless other scourges of humanity? Enough to talk around it, but not enough to address it honestly. In our culture, we don't really want the truth. What would anyone do with it? Stop advertising and selling products we don't need? Stop objectifying women? Stop chopping down forests? Not likely.

But if our mainstream culture can't handle the truth, there are those among us who hunger for it, who want more than anything to revive our spirits, who dream of a whole other way of life. There are those among us who understand, deep down in our bones, that our very survival (let alone our happiness) depends upon reclaiming the ancient wisdom of the spirit—that is, rediscovering it anew in an age of unprecedented pain and discord. This is the only hope for quieting the pain and getting back to our true purpose in life: to explore, create, and evolve. The spirit-body communication is our pathway to growth.

Evolution v. De-evolution

If the communication signals between spirit and body are weak or corrupted, the whole framework will break down and both will devolve.

As we've established, every sense we have (touch, vision, hearing, taste, smell, and of course that numinous sixth sense) communicates with the DNA to direct its next step. This information creates what we define as evolution: change governed by the interaction between a being and its environment. In this way, our sensory organs may be understood as *communication organs*. Their key feature is the ability to transmit information. They are our interplay between external and internal experience.

When the spirit and the body are exposed to too much dissonant stimulation, as is all too common in the modern world, their critical communication system begins to break down. The whole detector-probe system runs amok. Physical experience should communicate to the body whether an environment is unfavorable to its existence and help to make the body more viable within it. But in the world today, more often than not, that message either fails to send or is gravely misunderstood!

We are pretty far along the warped trajectory of de-evolution, where communication between the spirit and body is nearly defunct. We can see the clear examples of degenerating human DNA in the weakened offspring of our children (increased cases of physical and mental birth defects, earlier onsets of serious illness and cancer, etc.). Less obvious to most people is the atrophying of the spirit, which is equally reflected in the unraveling of the species.

This makes reclaiming our spirit-body connection extremely challenging. Meanwhile, a rash of cultural factors continues to deepen this disconnect, making it exponentially more difficult to overcome with each passing day. We have not only veered wildly off course, but, out of sheer inertia, we are continuing to travel further and further afield!

Our culturally driven quest to conquer the natural world—to think ourselves entitled to exploit nature as we like, to pursue riches and power at all costs, to dominate that which was never ours to take—has suffocated our spirit. It has made us sick in spirit, and thus also sick in body and in environment. Hypnotized by all the artificial trappings of wealth, vanity, status, and power, we've lost touch with that which is of real value. We've lost our equilibrium by over-flexing our destructive qualities (i.e., aggression, domination, ownership, etc.) and suppressing—and thus atrophying—our life-affirming qualities (i.e., strength, leadership, intuition, nurturance, creativity, etc.).

There is a wildness to that which is balanced and whole, yet the ultimate dictate of civilization is to stamp out all that is wild. Nature is wild, a force of life that resists domination and domestication. Our spirit is by nature wild—intuitive, alert, protective of its power; not to be confused with "mean," "crazy," and "unpredictable," which are cultural associations. Our spirit, like nature, revolts against domination.

It is argued that all the social laws and regulations have been created to provide checks and balances on human nature in order to maintain peaceful societies. Historically, however, such laws and regulations have served as much to sanction horrific acts of aggression and violence (just think, for example, of how the Europeans "settled" North America) as to protect the property of certain individuals. In the meantime, ironically enough, so many social regulations have alienated us from our spirits, which forever seek growth and balance within the greater construct of nature. But without the spirit, one cannot survive, much less evolve.

Once you truly see the link, once you truly recognize the value of a healthy, active spirit, you will want to do anything to get it back. The wholeness of your spirit will mean more to you than all of society's riches. This is a very good thing, because you will need a great deal of fight in you to get it back.

When you are ready, instead of using your mouth to quiet your spirit—by stuffing it with all manner of food and junk and sedatives—you will finally put it to proper use. Yes, you will rediscover the one tool that can call your spirit back into your body: *your voice.*

The Voice as Sensory Organ

The voice is the most important communication tool. It allows the spirit to report on its sensory experience. It might say "Ouch, that hurts!" or sing out with unfettered joy "The hills are alive with the sound of music!" But whatever it says, the voice is there to speak the *uncensored* truth of one's experience. It is the faithful interpreter of one's life experience.

If your voice only expressed an edited version of your experiences, would it be very useful? Would it have any use at all? If the voice is a tool for directing individual and communal life toward that which is life-generating, certainly a censor would only block its purpose. Censorship would arguably be dangerous, in effect exposing the individual or group to an undesirable end. If the information that the voice is communicating is unclear or incorrect, the consequences will be similarly messy.

At the most primal level, vocal expression directs life (not just among our species, but among all life, from dolphins to birds to crickets). To evolve in a life-generating direction requires that the web of life be allowed to engage in uninterrupted communication. Implicit in this is honesty, because anything less than honesty would only handicap the interconnected whole and all the individuated forms of consciousness within it. In other words, honesty is essential to the expression and evolution of life.

How much of what comes through the voice today is purely honest? Very little, I'm afraid. Yet, while we accept it as the social norm always to be editing and censoring and watering down our voices, who among us would knowingly agree to censor our other sensory organs—the eyes, ears, tongue, skin, etc.? But the voice, just as much as our other senses, is there to communicate the truth.

Here we are steeped in a world of censorship, of contrived and dishonest expression. How is the spirit supposed to work with that? How is it supposed to communicate without freedom of expression? What does that mean for our probe's (our body's) connection with our spirit? What does that mean for spiritual and evolutionary growth? It means that our whole system stammers, shuts up, and breaks down; that we de-spiral, individually and collectively, in a mutant direction. We can understand all of this as the result of gagging the spirit's voice.

Can you think of a time when your spirit spoke freely to an audience that didn't want to hear it, or couldn't understand it, or openly mocked it? Perhaps you can recall many such times. In any case, I bet it was an effective lesson about the need to censor—or even gag—yourself in order to fit in with the world around you. It probably taught you to restrict your mouth to the purpose of chewing and swallowing, not speaking your truth. In this way, the majority of us—starting at ever younger and younger ages—have been socially conditioned to sever the vocal cords of the spirit.

Without adult interference, children naturally speak honestly. Yet, they are constantly hushed and scolded, until their honest reflexes break down, turning them initially into white liars and then, eventually, into masters of manipulation. So much of socialization is learning how to lie appropriately, how to manipulate people—and therefore manipulate the levers of politics, business, and commerce. *We have all been raised to become not only good little consumers, but good little spin doctors.* We have been so immersed in this culture of dishonesty that we don't even think of it as dishonest—on the contrary, we tend to admire people for their ability to work the system just the way it is. We have been blinded to any alternative way of life. In this way, we have learned to be dishonest even with ourselves.

Most of us in this culture are spiritually impoverished from birth, just as those who raised us were. We've never been properly introduced to our spirit, yet it is always there, yearning to express itself. The more we ignore the spirit, the more it will leak through the cracks to rise up and make a great noise. We can feign deafness and attempt to place boundaries between our true feelings and the kind of life we're aiming (or instructed) to live. But there the neglected spirit will be, always tugging at us in the distorted form of an insatiable appetite—for affection, attention, money, food, drugs, escape—or in the form of anxiety, anger, rage, or anything else that will call attention to itself.

Who among us is free today to speak of our life-experience uncensored? Granted, the cult of confessional memoirs and reality TV shows runs rampant nowadays—but I am not talking about exhibitionistic, opportunistic, prepackaged, airbrushed storytelling to obtain fame and fortune. I am asking: Who among us will dare speak truthfully about our personal suffering, our daily struggles, our dissatisfactions with our lives, our loneliness and innermost disappointments as an act of honest spiritual expression? People who speak honestly, who care more for the truth than for social acceptance, are rare birds indeed.

If you want to reconnect with your spirit, it's not too late—as long as you are prepared to make a deliberate, fully conscious, courageous effort to tap into your innermost self. Over the years, the socially conditioned individual has accumulated many protective layers to prevent the truth from leaking in or out, so it will take some time to peel them back.

Fortunately, the spirit is a resilient force. Writes Clarissa Pinkola Estes in *Women Who Run With the Wolves*, "the soul and the spirit have resources that are astonishing. Like wolves and other creatures, the soul and spirit are able to thrive on very little and sometimes for a long time on nothing."

But when the spirit is forced to remain silent for a long while, it is not without a price. That price can be many things. Here's a sampling: violence against the self (including assaulting oneself with food and other substances), violence against others, permitting others to violate one's boundaries (whether physical, emotional, or psychological), voluntary victimization, domination of others, and excessive self-control. Pretty much any type of imbalanced behavior is the price to be paid for a starved, gagged, or otherwise enslaved spirit.

Hence, rule number one for living: *Don't ignore the spirit. To do so is tantamount to denying the self. And to deny the self is to deny nature, which is the cradle of life.* Yet our culture has trained us to live like obedient dogs under the hand of a strict master. It deprives us of our wild natures, our precious instincts and intuitions, and renders us domesticated. Thus, we predictably step into line, as mere cogs in the wheels of the great industrial-political machine that we call civilization.

It is a self-perpetuating cycle: our culture needs its loyal subjects to exist, and these loyal subjects, who are no longer able to fend for themselves in the wild, are dependent on their masters to survive. In this way, we humans have largely forgotten who and what we are, and with each generation we become less human and more hybrid. What's worse, we don't even know why this is so, for the trail home is all but forgotten, and our voices are barely strong enough to call for help.

The Way Out Is In

The only way out is *in*—inward to the spirit. The only way into the spirit is through the voice of honest expression. The spirit will not accept anything less than truth, and truth is what poses the greatest threat to our culture. In this day and age, to unleash the spirit and give it free expression requires a warrior's resolve. It's much easier to tell the truth to a toilet bowl, or to shut the mouth entirely, than to speak out bravely from one's depths. It's easier not to speak, or to stuff the mouth so full that no intelligible sound can possibly come out.

Domesticated humans are trained servants of a cultural agenda. Now, granted, if you are born into this, you'll mistake it for normal until something jolts you out of the hypnosis. Often, this requires a breakdown of sorts, a state of emergency so great that your spirit makes itself known to you. Very often, the spirit will rattle the cage through the pain of emotional eating or some other substance abuse.

This is why our most painful self-abusive behaviors can be our greatest gifts. Instead of projecting that anger, pain, and dissatisfaction onto the world—blaming our parents, our spouses, society, or Murphy's Law—we simply need to say: *Wow, look at that. My spirit is speaking through this pain and dysfunction. Let me see if I can hear what it is saying... What's that? It's telling my brain to get the heck out of the way and let it drive. It's asking me to look honestly at what I've agreed to in this world, at the stories I've accepted about myself, at my sense of purpose, at the values I place on everything, at all the things I do on auto-pilot. How frightening to wake up to all of this! But scared as I am, I'm willing to listen and keep listening. Maybe it will lead me to make enough changes to the structure of my life to stop damaging myself and those I love. I must stop ignoring my spirit. I've become too complacent, too familiar with addiction, which doesn't fulfill me. But what would happen if I really tuned into my spirit? What would that unleash? I sense that my spirit is too wild for my mind. Others will think me crazy. It might just make my life more complicated...*

Just keep asking the questions as they come to you, and stay very, very present for the sometimes searing but ultimately liberating truth.

A friend of mine recently told me that after years of internal struggle, she agreed to appease her husband by visiting a psychiatrist. To make a long story short, she was put on a popular antidepressant. For a month she was productive, confident, and "happy." She explained that the down side of taking her prescribed medication was terrible—the come-downs after the good stretches were extreme, and in her clean-celled, sensitized body, the symptoms (including headaches, difficulty sleeping, depression, bloating, etc.) were even more acute. We both found it scary that taking such drugs could cover up—indeed muffle—an entire persona. On drugs, one can go through life without ever hearing the spirit speak or acting upon its wisdom. Yet, even in a drugged body, the spirit always tugs, matching the cover-up inch for inch in some way that plagues the individual.

There is a price to be paid for reclaiming your spirit. It is not cheap. It means valuing it more than you value the way you are perceived in your peer group or by your family. It is a price few are willing to pay, but those who do would pay it again and again for its unparalleled, life-generating powers.

Expect to feel by turns torn and scared, euphoric and empowered, fractured and whole. Expect new sensations of inner silence as you quiet the raging storm within. Expect that silence to be at once soothing and unsettling. Don't expect predictability. Don't expect a linear path. The path to the spirit is a labyrinth. You'll have to surrender to a great, organic process that you may not always fully comprehend. But like a tree, the deeper your roots can go, the higher you'll grow. When you reunite with your spirit, you grow spherically in every spiritual direction. You become able to hold more: more feeling, more compassion, more understanding, more experience.

If you are looking only to get high, not deep, take a happy pill. If you are looking for an easy fix, you'll never reach your spirit. If you are looking for superficial beauty, you'll never recognize its cheapness until you've experienced real beauty. If you are afraid of chaos, of being wrong, of sometimes feeling alone, you may not be ready for the truth. I encourage you to look those fears in the eye and let them evolve into strengths. After generation upon generation of enslaving the spirit, it's going to take some muscle and courage to bring it back in full force. But what could possibly be more important or timely than to bring the spirit back? How many more days, months, years, decades, and lifetimes of disordered eating can you stand?

For lack of spiritual observation and navigation, we humans are literally failing to evolve—we are literally mutating (genetically, emotionally, mentally) as a species. Through our computerized, programmed brains, we are letting destructive powers direct our choices. We are dehumanizing ourselves, my friends. Yes, the brain is essential to our functioning, but it is no spiritual leader! The brain is extraordinary for relaying information throughout the body, but it will never succeed alone as captain of our being.

In our mechanistic world, the spirit is crying out against its devaluation. This is the root of all stress, anger, self-loathing, binging and purging, overeating and sulking, taking drugs, and living in constant fear and anxiety. This is the spirit's last-ditch attempt to signal S.O.S.! Heed your pain, and it will be your gateway to wholeness.

Do you think you're alone in your despair? Do you think those polished housewives with their perfect legs and platinum hair, with their Manolo Blahniks and Jimmy Choo handbags, are immune to your breed of despair? Well, if you think this, you're wrong. I know for a fact that you're wrong, because such women have told me all about their despair. Perhaps you are one of them. For ten years, one polished Manhattanite after another has come to me seeking relief from their despair. Even if they are adept at keeping up appearances—even if to all the world they appear like models of perfection, with not a hair out of place—they too feel the terrible disconnect between their inner and outer lives. They are trapped: damned if they follow their spirit and live honestly, damned if they don't. Again, honesty comes at a price that few are willing to pay.

Our sessions are private and confidential. But, gee wiz, if only these individuals would speak up and tell their friends, their communities, their own daughters how they really feel! Of course, the "haves" are the most afraid of exposing their ugly truths because they've spent their whole lives trying to look beautiful and together, to portray themselves as beacons of sophistication. The last thing they want, after investing years of time and money and emotional energy into cultivating an image, is to show the eyesore behind the façade. But to those of us who have come to the same crossroads and dared to bare all, it's clear that real beauty cannot be achieved without, first, this honest unveiling.

The world is full of cowards covering up the truth, and we all fall prey to cowardice at one time or another. I'll tell you exactly what I told this friend who briefly took the antidepressants she was prescribed: "There is no drug better than courage. There is no high greater than honesty. There is no achievement more admirable than saving your spirit. Want to help others? Want to make a contribution to the world? Want to heal the planet or be philanthropic? Above all, be honest with yourself, and you will not only save yourself, you will save the spirits of countless others whose lives you touch."

The ultimate heroic act is saving your own spirit. Surely, what you transform within will manifest without. Again, to quote Clarissa Pinkola Estes from *Women Who Run with the Wolves*, "Although a woman may not be able to stop the dissection of culture and lands overnight, she can stop doing so to her own body."

If you are abusing food or other substances or activities, make no mistake, your spirit is rattling its cage. You've allowed lies to infiltrate your life—to take you, a perfectly good coyote, and turn you into a cocker spaniel! You can ignore the truth for as long as it takes to lead you hopelessly astray, or you can choose the honest path back to yourself and to your life. As long as you ignore the truth, you will experience the haunting of the spirit—and, believe me, you will *never* be able to quench your spiritual thirst with food.

I'll say it again: the only way out is in, into the spirit. And there's only one way into the spirit, through honesty. How honest can you be? Ask yourself this simple question: "What does my deepest self desire?" Then ask yourself: "How would my life be different if I achieved this?" If this is truly your deepest wish, you have no other choice than to pursue it. If you ignore it, you will keep stuffing yourself with false nourishment, which will just leave you feeling empty, voiceless, and ashamed.

As we have established, this modern world is no place for the human spirit. Society attempts to shut it down from birth. We accept stories about ourselves that have nothing to do with who and what we really are. The things that have happened to us are not who we are. We may have external attributes or handicaps that have brought us praise or degradation. But those things are not who we are. Yet, we weave a story about ourselves based on these things and that story becomes the place holder for our self-identification. Once this story is locked in place, we play it out. It pigeon-holes us. We become doomed to play out the story again and again until we realize it's just a silly illusion that can be dissolved at any moment. To cope with the perversions of our world, we take in substances that destroy our physical, mental, and emotional pathways and reduce our true desires to chemical addictions— such that we ache for truth while we reach for our poison.

On the one hand, we are addicted to all the "normal" foods that comprise the mainstream diet: processed grains, animal products, so-called health foods, soda, alcohol, and all the other usual suspects. On the other hand, we are stuck in a socially programmed environment that undermines our most valuable, life-generating instincts. Together, our addictions and our environment all but destroy the spirit—yet we limp along, our spirits still struggling to communicate, someway, somehow.

The spirit and the culturally determined self work in diametrically opposed pursuits. The former longs to feel, to create, to connect and conduct with the natural world, whereas the latter seeks acceptance and the rewards of social status. The former seeks light and nourishment, whereas the latter throws up walls and limitations. It is an unconscious war between the two selves, a constant state of internal warfare. When you find yourself in a holding pattern of overeating, purging, starving yourself, or taking in other harmful substances, it's because *you are literally at war with yourself.*

Make no mistake, the spirit is a tremendous force of nature. If it needs to, it will hold you by the jugular of your addictions until you surrender to the truth: that something is dreadfully wrong. The social roles that we typically play to obscure our true natures can only hold up for so long. Eventually, if we ever want the pain to stop, we must face up to ourselves—warts and all.

Water the Spirit with Love, not War

Through the body, the spirit is always exploring and experiencing the physical world, forever drawing greater and greater connections and expanding its range of understanding. The spirit's most vital aide in this endeavor is love.

Once again, I turn to Almine for her wonderfully lucid definitions of emotions, such that I've never found elsewhere. In this case, her definition of love is extremely helpful. *Love*, says Almine, *is the desire to include.* This conception of love has helped me understand how probing into the deepest, darkest parts of oneself with a real desire to understand and grow can lead to greater self-love and compassion for others. And ultimately, nothing is more liberating and joyous than the power of love.

In other words, the more we reject about ourselves, the less we love ourselves. The more we understand and accept—that is, *include*—parts of our true selves, the more we can love ourselves and can come to understand and accept others. The problem is that, from childhood onward, we have been told that we are either too much or not enough—too tall, or not tall enough; too thin, or not thin enough; too strong, or not strong enough; too clever, or not clever enough; too sensitive, or not sensitive enough; and on and on. The list of inadequacies is endless. We have been divided up into parts and our parts have been placed into separate categories—those things that are worthy of social acceptance, and those other things that we spend our lives despising.

We are taught to examine every body part and character trait, and accept or reject it according to the prescribed social standard. And then, as if this were not brutal enough, everything in our environment is designed to reinforce that message, making us ashamed, neurotic, vain, narcissistic—or all of these things at once. We simply cannot honor a body that we subconsciously reject. When we over-eat or under-eat, or binge and purge, we are enacting war against ourselves. If we let it go on too long, such a war can result in suicide.

In such a war, we must look more closely at the "enemy": what exactly have we rejected in ourselves, and why? We must bring our entire selves—both the supposedly desirable and supposedly undesirable parts—out into the light and embrace them as parts of a whole, of a human being who is suffering for lack of love and nourishment.

This is not a process that happens overnight. Self-knowledge comes in stages and layers, even if you are in full, dedicated pursuit of it. Going into these dark places is never fun, but like a miner, you'll be amazed at what you'll shine your flashlight on in those deep caves of your soul. I can tell you this because I have been there. I've gone into petrifying, dark places within myself that I thought I would never emerge from. Each time, I've wondered if I'll survive it. Each time, I've emerged with treasure that exceeds that of the previous expedition—treasure that makes me spiritually bigger, fuller, more able to accept, love, and appreciate the great wonders of life. *It is the journey from self-assault to self-love.* To take this journey is to recover, step by step, the natural equanimity of the spirit.

Whenever I emerge from such a journey, I remind myself as a reinforcement for the next time: *You'll go into dark, scary places that may seem to have no end and bring bottomless pain. But you have been to such places before, and you have always come out into the bright, heart-soaring light. Apply your highest knowledge to this journey, and you will see and feel even more than before.* This tool really helps me because, as we know, there's never an end point to our growth, and there will doubtless be more daunting journeys to take and caves to explore along the way. It's good to be prepared; an explorer needs a compass, maps, and a reliable vehicle—be it a well-built ship, a conditioned body, or a good pair of shoes. In my explorer's kit, I keep my highest knowledge, my experience, and the above note-to-self. What's in your kit?

Only by venturing deep within ourselves can we come to accept ourselves and halt the self-destruction. Only by facing head-on that which makes us want to turn away can we overcome the worst aspects of our social conditioning. Self-hatred is the essence of prejudice, and one leads inevitably to the next, to the point where entire groups and races of people are excluded from standards of social acceptance. But you cannot overcome prejudice until you first dissolve the conflict within. As a human being, you have an immense capacity to understand and love the life that resides within and all around you—but in the world today, you must swim against the deadly currents of convention to tap into it. To learn to love yourself is to become more fully human, to reclaim your spirit, and it is the only hope for overcoming emotional eating.

In the hustle and bustle of our lives, it's all too easy to forget the gift that our bodies are: to live in a sensory body—to experience life in all its richness and variation, on so many levels of comprehension—is the ultimate gift! When the going gets tough, remember this, and know that there is untold treasure waiting to be discovered in the dark places of your soul. You are doing yourself a great service when you heed your suffering, when you seek to understand your behaviors, not ignore them.

Often light-seekers and theologians will dismiss the physical in the pursuit of the spiritual. That is a grave mistake. Right here on earth, in a body, is the place to be. It's where alchemy happens, where we can experience darkness and make it known. Right here—in this peculiar world that is so frequently at war with itself, just as we are so frequently at war with our bodies—is where magic can happen, where the spirit can suddenly grow in leaps and bounds.

I urge you to start listening to yourself right now. Consider, what are your problems trying to tell you? Why are you overeating? What emptiness are you trying to fill? Or, conversely, why are you purging or starving yourself? Don't you have a right to exist? Don't you deserve love and nourishment? Now is the time to begin honoring your body and your spirit in earnest. Listen to what they are telling you. Stop muffling your voice.

Should you decide to unlock the cage that's been holding your spirit captive and that has made you an enemy of your body, be gentle on yourself. Take your time. Take extra care. This is not a race. Every step in the direction of reuniting your spirit with your body will further dissolve the darkness of your thoughts and behaviors.

Don't speak of this important personal journey in casual company. At first, when you are with others, I recommend that you listen more than you speak. Listen and think, ease yourself into this new way of perceiving. Surround yourself with people who genuinely support you, not with those who will pull you back into the old destructive cycles. Treat yourself a bit like a patient. Reintroducing the spirit to the body is an essential stage of convalescence. As you embark on this journey of healing, remember to rest, reflect, and enjoy your reunion with yourself.

PART IV

The Journey Back to Balance:
Practical Steps and Exercises

The Game Plan

To live in the modern world is to spend a lifetime banishing the pieces of yourself that don't neatly fit the cultural plan, the accepted social structures, or some authority's interpretation of who you should be. Most mainstream approaches to childrearing stunt natural development and indoctrinate innocent little hearts and minds with dangerous misinformation. Undesirable traits are systematically replaced with ideas, behaviors, and stories designed to keep everyone in line as loyal citizens of a misguided world. But where have those original pieces of ourselves gone? Make no mistake: they are still there, lodged deep in our unconscious minds, as we'll explore further in the coming pages.

From the moment we're born, continuing well into adulthood, and right up until the day we resolve to do something about it, we grow further and further from our authentic selves. We literally deny ourselves the most natural yearnings of our hearts, our bodies, and our souls to make room for "real life," which, more often than not, directly opposes our highest good.

Deep down, however, we all know our true worth. Something deep within us, by the very nature of our humanity, knows we are designed to be beautiful and healthy, to experience soul-quenching love, to emit love from a wide-open heart, and to find inspiration in every breath we take.

As we've already discussed in the preceding chapters, social conditioning and separation consciousness have crushed the human spirit. But even if we cannot immediately remedy this phenomenon on a large scale, we can begin right now to remedy it for ourselves. It takes courage and a very strong desire, but if we put all our faculties to work we will start moving step by soul-satisfying step toward becoming whole, balanced, human.

To that end, we must take the following steps:

1. Build healthy boundaries.
2. Implement and internalize the Sacred Rules.
3. Embark on the Journey of the Hero.
4. Gather up and reassemble the broken pieces, and proceed as a reconstituted whole.

Sound good? One last thing before we begin building boundaries. Allow me to introduce you to that invisible someone who has been sabotaging you all your life…

The Stimulation Monster

Not unlike the yeast monster I refer to in *Detox 4 Women*, the stimulation monster drives us to do things we would not choose of our own volition. Or if we choose them, it is because we are wired to think of them as pleasures. We have been wired since birth for constant stimulation, not peace, and this cultural phenomenon is only getting worse.

What is stimulation? We consider stress and anxiety as negative forces in our everyday lives, and rightly so. However, compulsive shopping, eating, socializing, entertaining, and sexual activity are generally categorized as normal and desirable. However, the causes of stress and anxiety and such compulsive activities are the flip sides of the same coin: stimulation. No matter how pleasing the stimulation feels, stimulation by its very nature corrodes our peace and sovereignty. We are culturally wired to seek out these stimulations as positive experiences—so much so that we all become addicts of whatever stimulations are produced and marketed for our consumption. Sure, there are lesser evils among them, but anything acidic will have an addictive effect equal to the degree of its acidity.

The key is to discern what those stimulating addictions are for you, and to experience even brief moments of absolute non-stimulation so that you can start to feel the difference. Once you feel what the absence of stimulation feels like and how empowering it is, you'll want to spend more time in that state. As a practice, you'll want to elongate those moments of non-stimulation and experience them more frequently. But don't confuse non-stimulation with meditation. The key is to enter a state of non-stimulation before you eat. This will help to prevent overeating. Food manufacturers typically overload their products with addictive stimulants—the most common among them being salt, sugars, starches, and caffeine—to keep you coming back for more. This is to say nothing of drugs and alcohol. Our whole culture is geared toward stimulating, addictive behavior.

Releasing yourself from the grip of artificial stimulation—food by food, substance by substance, habit by habit—is what this work is all about. If the process isn't always easy, if you stick with it, the rewards are nothing short of extraordinary!

Exercise: Achieve a State of Non-stimulation

It is tricky to describe non-stimulation and even trickier to achieve because it's so foreign to modern life, but it's well worth a try. Start by just sitting in a chair or on the floor. There should be no media or conversation whatsoever in your space. If there is activity outside, notice it but do not hook into it. As much as possible, focus on existing without any effort. Just breathe and pay attention to what you see, hear, feel, and experience inside and outside your body. For example, you might just look out the window at the sky, notice your breath without trying to breathe differently, and simply notice your surroundings without dwelling on anything specific.

How will you know when you are not being stimulated? You will merge with your experience, rather than merely hover outside of it as an observer. It is a childlike state, when you have no cares or attachments, when you are simply and unselfconsciously enjoying the air, the pulse of the body, the singing of birds. You will feel engaged with the world, part of its very fabric, not something separate. There is no desire in this state: thought is inseparable from experience. Again, this is so foreign to our modern mindset that it's hard to describe, and yet that's precisely why it's so valuable to experience.

The goal is to abstain from stimulation until you reconnect with the web of life. From this state you simply cannot self-abuse because you are not caught up in the self. You are supported by a peaceful, satisfying energy. Before eating, reconnect with this world of energy, this web of life, of which you are a vital part. If you don't, you will be far more vulnerable to unsatisfying eating patterns, which reduce the nutrient value of your food. I strongly recommend taking a few minutes before each meal to quiet the stimulation monster in this way. Then, when you eat, notice the difference in how you eat, how you breathe as you eat, how you taste the food more fully, how you chew longer and feel satisfied sooner without having to count calories or measure portion sizes. Engage your consciousness before you consume anything at all.

Boundaries: Growing Up Unprotected

Now, let's talk about boundaries. Without healthy boundaries, we are left vulnerable to all kinds of dangers. This section is about finally, thoughtfully erecting those boundaries, and tailoring them to a very complex and constantly shifting world. With healthy boundaries we are sovereign, like a country with a strong government and military that cannot be penetrated and plundered. Without them we are homeless, unprotected, impotent captives of whatever stronger forces come along.

You might find it a little ironic that in order to achieve the higher goal of unity consciousness it is necessary to erect strong boundaries. On the surface they may seem in conflict. Look closer and you'll see that boundaries between parts of a whole are essential. Each part of an interdependent whole must function healthily on an individual level in order to serve the viability of the whole. Any functional life form has distinct boundaries and a distinct role within the larger web of life. The healthier your boundaries are, the better you serve yourself as well as the larger communities to which you belong.

Now let's think about this in terms of your body: if your blood is impure, it will not serve the wholeness of your body. If your cells have no boundaries, your metabolism will go haywire. If you let in all kinds of toxins, acids, and addictive stimulants, your brain and body chemistry will reconfigure themselves to expect and crave these substances, despite all the damage they do to every part of your body. Meanwhile, you are compromising your very spirit. You can dismantle the whole by compromising its smallest components, just as you can render the smaller components defunct by poisoning the whole directly. Therefore, to tackle emotional eating, you must protect yourself from the inside and out.

Everything in life relies on strong boundaries. Cells have cell walls; atoms have atomic belts; even wave particles have vibratory differentiation that make one distinct from another. When waters become stagnant and grow poisoned with bacteria it is because the bacteria is able to infiltrate and dominate. Decomposition is triggered and completed by the infestation of decomposers. Weakened boundaries simply break once the enemy becomes too strong. Boundaries protect our individuality against corrupt forces while letting in our allies.

With boundaries, you can be both strong and gentle and help others find their own sovereignty. When you feel safe and secure enough in your own body, when you are strong in spirit and self-regard, you'll no longer feel threatened by all the outside forces that would usurp your world. Sovereign people don't bottle up all their frustrations and then fly off the handle at the drop of a hat, or behave passive-aggressively, or deny themselves for days and then eat whole bags of cookies and tubs of ice cream.

A lack of boundaries indicates a lack of self-respect, and lack of self-respect is arguably the seed of all evil. How can you expect anyone else to respect you if you don't respect yourself? By the same token, how will you ever respect other people and other lives if you don't properly honor your own life? You cannot control how others feel about you or the standards to which they hold you. However, most people will respond positively to a beautiful spirit, and that's not something you can fake. A pure and loving spirit must emanate from a healthy, secure, self-respecting place. Once you understand this, you will gladly relinquish control over other people's perceptions—and that is essential to throwing off the shackles of emotional eating!

From birth we become receptacles of dangerous cultural philosophies. Most of us were never taught the laws of nature, the principles of cause and effect, or the importance of a cultivated consciousness. With so many misguided adults leading them into the world, children cannot be faulted for accepting all the social myths as truths, or for becoming strangers to their authentic selves. We are all children who have grown up, and we should not blame ourselves for the indoctrinations of our elders.

Now that we are adults, however, we can repair much of the psychic and physical damage and put our pieces back together again. The first step is to recognize our own folly, the ways in which we set ourselves up for failure, and how these patterns have been ingrained in us from day one. If you have read this far, chances are you have already embarked upon this vital first step. Be proud of this accomplishment, because it requires an independent mind in the face of very powerful social forces that keep most people blind to their cycles of self-abuse. You are here because you want to stand up for yourself, and that's absolutely essential, because no one else can do it for you!

Even so, you might be feeling intimidated by the strength and resolve it takes to heal. If that's the case, please know that I have been where you are. I know how it feels to falter, to lose heart, to feel unequal to the challenges ahead. But I have fought and persisted my way out of the jungle of poisoned perspectives to a place of clarity, sovereignty, self-respect, and love for my fellow travelers. This is not to say I'm always one hundred percent in the clear. But if I still falter from time to time, at least I know it's by my own hand—not at the whims and judgments of others.

Erecting healthy boundaries is not optional. If you want to be free, you need to be sovereign, not a marionette of social programs, cultural mores, and propaganda. You need strong self-government and attentive warriors. You will lay every brick, and you will keep watch over your surroundings for those who would usurp your power.

But remember, the point is not to build walls around yourself like an abused child trying to shut out feelings. Not remotely. This kind of boundary building simply allows you to live according to life-generating principles in a world that doesn't understand or value them. These boundaries will allow you to become more connected, to conduct more feeling, by protecting you from the assaults of all the world's nonsense. You will choose what to let in. You will create the necessary space to use your discretion.

Of course, you will have to make some difficult choices if your boundaries are going to be of any use. You will identify certain people, ideologies, behaviors, events, and life plans as threatening to your balanced sovereign state and, at least for a while, you may have to keep them at bay. If you allow these negative forces in for tea, particularly when you are vulnerable and "under construction," you'll run the risk of setbacks. Before you know it, an innocent cup of tea may turn into an orgy of emotional eating.

Only you know what is safe to allow in, and only you know your own courage against willful foes. With practice, you will get better at judging the circumstances and securing the drawbridge as necessary. It will all come down to how much you want to recover your sovereignty.

Exercise: Build Healthy Boundaries

Make a list of the top ten things you don't want to engage in anymore, such as certain relationships, behaviors, and habits. Then, one by one, go through the list and imagine each one and how it makes you feel. For each item, say emphatically out loud: "I DO NOT WANT TO _____ ANYMORE." Then really imagine the situation. Really imagine how it makes you feel. See if you can track where you feel it in your body. Then, when you're certain you don't want to do it anymore, say emphatically out loud: "I WILL NOT _____ ANYMORE."

Perhaps you want to stop shopping for clothes whenever you feel stressed or unappreciated; or stop fighting with your teenaged kid rather than talking things out calmly; or stop spending every spare moment of your day trying to please other people rather than carving out time for yourself. Some things on your list may be very serious, such as tolerating a difficult relationship with a lot of painful history, unkind words, or outright abuse. Begin to snip the cords that are strangling you and leaching your life force, blocking your truth, making your life a lie. Don't throw the towel in on a perfectly salvageable relationship, but do take a good look and don't be afraid to see what might be poisoning your life.

One at a time, focus on eliminating each energetic vampire from your life. We can't even begin to conquer emotional eating if we remain emotionally controlled by things that lead us to situations we hate in our daily lives. Pay attention. Really pay attention, and you'll likely come up with far more than ten things that you don't want to do anymore, and you'll ask yourself why the heck you've tolerated them for as long as you have. Now you're getting closer to self-love. Now you're getting closer to your spirit. Now you're beginning to see the pieces of yourself that split apart when you learned how to be a receptacle for other people's ideas, stories, and motives. Trust your expanding consciousness, not in some new age-y way, but in a practical, tangible way that affects each moment of your life.

As you begin this process, other people might get scared to see you changing. They might attempt to keep you in your old mindset, to preserve the dynamic to which they've become accustomed. If you are firm and stay true to your vision, you will earn their respect and they will eventually cease interference. So don't back down, lest you fall back into your old rut and lose not only their respect, but, more importantly, your own!

If there are negative people in your life whom you can't easily ignore or stay away from, remember these tips:

- Be really aware of their issues. Neither slip into their vortex nor let them penetrate your spirit.

- Listen without trying to control. If they cannot see or hear anything but themselves, any advice you offer will lead only to further discord and frustration.

- Know your limits in the presence of that person's distress.

This requires a strong foundation, so you must strengthen yours if it is weak. What do you believe about life? Who are the most important people in it, and why? What truly makes you happy and fills your life with love, light, hope, clarity, and creativity? And what takes those things away from you? Let your vision of what you want to make of your life determine what you want to eliminate from it. This approach is one of practical, positive transition, rather than of militantly unrealistic, negative declarations.

For example, instead of saying, "I hate Bill and I don't want to be his friend," try: "I love Todd. He's so kind and thoughtful and supportive. I would like to spend more time with him." If you are making more time for the people who serve your highest good, you will naturally spend less time with those who undermine you in order to serve their own unhealthy needs. If you must maintain contact with that negative person, keep it cordial and short. Don't energize the relationship. Try to create healthy boundaries and move on. If you seem stuck in a toxic relationship despite your best efforts, ask yourself, "What is keeping me here? Why don't I stick up for myself and move on?"

Similarly, instead of saying "I'm going to quit drinking coffee now," try this: "I'm going to start drinking vegetable juice every morning." Sure, you might still have some coffee later, but the juice will give you a wonderful charge and leave you feeling so clean that, eventually, having the coffee won't make sense to your life anymore.

If the exercises required for achieving emotional and social freedom are sometimes thorny and complex, the exercises for achieving physical freedom are more cut and dried. Do you want a clean-celled body? Well, you have to transition to alkaline foods and clean your intestine consistently over a significant period of time. Work it into your schedule. Make it your priority.

The Sacred Rules

As long as you are still deeply hooked on food stimulation, it's important that you hold fast to these Sacred Rules. They are designed to prevent cycles of emotional eating while the tensions between your behaviors and emotions are so delicate.

1. **Eat only what is designated for you.** Eat and drink only what you have consciously determined serves your highest good—i.e., the foods recommended in *Detox 4 Women, The Raw Food Detox Diet, The Rose Cleanse,* or another transition plan that makes sense for you now. Be sure it's food that either you've prepared for yourself or that has been prepared specifically for you according to your plan. DO NOT eat your children's food, your spouse's food, food that others randomly bring into your space (at the office, in the classroom, etc.), or any acidic foods unfit for human consumption according to the rules of acidity and alkalinity.

2. **Eat light to heavy.** The light-to-heavy principle is the simplest guide of what and when to consume. This really helps to break destructive, haphazard eating patterns and sets you up for success. Here are a few guidelines: Do not eat your first meal according to your watch. Rather, listen to your body. If you are not hungry for lunch at noon, wait until you are hungry. Start with hydrating, high-vibration substances and move on to denser substances by the end of the day. For example, start with chi by breathing in life force energy from fresh air and sunshine. When your body asks for more, start with water, and then move on to vegetable juice when needed. Ideally, you will not eat or even want to eat until you have assimilated vegetable juice. Do the best you can as you adapt to this way of ordered eating, bearing in mind that what works best today will evolve as your cells become cleaner.

3. **Prepare, prepare, prepare, especially for restaurants and social situations.** Do not make excuses such as "Oh, I was just so hungry" or "That's all there was at the ball park" or "The

salad didn't satisfy me so I picked at everyone else's plates." The best way to prevent such excuses is never to go to a restaurant starving. Have some carrots or other crudités (perhaps with a yummy dip like homemade guacamole) or cabbage-and-goat-cheese wraps, olives, or other favorite vegetable-centric snack to take the edge off your hunger beforehand. Restaurants and social events are rarely designed to serve your highest good or ensure complete nutritional satisfaction, particularly if you have a big appetite. Know yourself; know what you like; know where you're going (go online and read the menu or call). Don't be afraid to take a few things along with you, like a baggie packed with extra baby greens, goat cheese, avocado, lemon, stevia, carrots, and chocolate. That's what I do! Too embarrassed? Get over it. This is your life. Social programming is what got you into this mess of emotional eating; don't let it prevent you from getting out of it. I'd rather draw a few sideways looks or even critical comments than sacrifice my sovereignty. If people think you're too difficult, you're hanging around with the wrong crowd. Preparation ensures satisfaction.

4. Find your sweet spot before eating, or else stick to raw veggies. Your sweet spot is a peaceful state of non-stimulation (see page 89) and heightened awareness that helps dispel mindless eating. However, asking yourself to avoid all mindless eating may be unrealistic at this stage, so if you must nosh before you find your sweet spot, stick to raw vegetables. If you're shopping, or at a movie, or still at the office and your whole body is urging you toward food, and you just cannot find the space in your schedule to find your sweet spot, pull out your bag of veggies—but reach for *nothing else*. Remember, even if you feel in control, you are still an addict. Satiate that urge to dig your teeth into something with a pound of carrots, beets, jicama, or cherry tomatoes and make peace with your lot, just as drug addicts must make peace with abstinence and redirect their cravings.

Exercise: Find Your Sweet Spot

There are several ways you can center yourself and get into your sweet spot. Do what you can with the time you have and you'll find the most effective, creative ways to center. With practice, it will become easier to find and hold your peace, and the sweet spot will become a natural mental resting place for you. Here are some ideas to get you started:

- Sit quietly and witness whatever thoughts are vying for attention in your mind. Then move beyond them by paying attention to your immediate environment and the way various parts of your body feel, as described in the previous non-stimulation exercise (see page 79).
- If you are at the office, instead of eating at your desk, take a walk or two around the block before you eat lunch. This will stretch your mental energy before it can recalcify in the old rut of emotional eating.
- Take a bath. Immerse yourself for as long as it takes to feel centered. Allow the water to help you reconnect with your emotions and become peacefully aware of your body. The water will also pull off the stifling levels of electromagnetic energy piled on top of you from modern living that can affect the quality of your eating and sleeping.
- Wherever you are, consider something critical that someone has said to you. Bring it fully to mind and see if you can get to the bottom of (1) how and why it bothered you; (2) what social programming was behind it; (3) what story about yourself it either reinforced or changed; (4) how, in the honest, peaceful light of non-

stimulation, it helps you better understand the effect your behavior has on others. Then take a few deep, mindful breaths. Once you find your sweet spot, all the hyperactivity, neediness, lustfulness, anxiety, and stress of the world can be seen for what they are. They will no longer have a hold on you. And instead of judging them, you can learn from them, making them worth their weight in gold.

5. Exercise is non-negotiable. Not because you should be looking to burn calories. Instead, exercise because you are so drenched in stimulation and the life-deteriorating energy that stagnates in your physical and etheric/chi pathways. Such stagnation leads to accumulation and calcification, which will turn you into a monster—literally and figuratively! Your body will twist and stiffen and suffocate in these sluggish energy patterns, and your attitude, thoughts, and words will reflect them. Unless you want to degenerate in a repellant downward spiral, get moving! It doesn't matter when or where, though outdoors is always best. And it doesn't matter what you do, as long as you avoid high-impact aerobics, such as running on concrete in a body carrying more than twenty extra pounds (despite the common wisdom about weight-bearing activities, use common sense and consider what all that pounding with excess weight does internally). If you're not carrying extra weight and enjoy high-impact aerobics or long runs, by all means, go for it but be aware that running on concrete is not ideal. Try to find a dirt track, run barefoot on the beach or keep your road-runs short. Instead, walk, swim, ride a bike, use a rowing machine, or dance around to your favorite music. There will always be excuses for not exercising, but those days when you think you can go without it will often turn out to be the days when you need it most. Make physical activity sacred. There are too many life-deteriorating forces at play in our world not to engage your body as a powerful, limber warrior of peace and self-sovereignty!

6. Be clear about your transition foods, and always combine properly. If you have some fish, then it would be breaking the sacred rule to start eating pasta or bread too. This is a really clean way to keep from binge eating. If you must have more, order some more salad with goat cheese, or another piece of fish. (I actually ordered a second fish as part of a three-course pre-fix dinner one night on my honeymoon in Hawaii. The chef agreed to give me another plate of fish in lieu of dessert. It was the most succulent sea bass. It did the trick. I was happily satiated, and a happy wife makes for a happy husband, as any married man knows!)

7. Be comfortable when you eat. If you are in a place or position that is not pleasing to you, your meal will not satisfy you, which means you'll probably keep eating. Do not eat while standing, walking, or driving. If you need to eat a meal over the course of a long trip, that's okay, but this should be a rare exception. If you need to eat in the car because you have a long commute, stick to only raw or properly cooked vegetables, or a bit of fruit. Eating dense foods while in transit is a very bad habit—it's almost always more about feeding your addiction and drowning your boredom than any sort of necessary nourishment. Furthermore, you won't digest well in transit. Many people actually eat *because* they are uncomfortable. They feel antsy, there is poor chi flow in the room, or someone with negative energy has entered their space (such as a grumpy spouse coming home after a bad day at work). If this is a familiar situation for you, take a moment to close your eyes and think about where you would be comfortable and go there. If necessary, politely excuse yourself from the room. By the time you return, the mood will have shifted and you will have avoided noshing outside the healthy boundaries of your sacred plan.

8. Don't eat when stressed or angry. Yes, we already discussed finding your sweet spot prior to eating, but this is an extra reinforcement should there arise an unexpected drama or stressful situation. Not only will even the most alkaline substances such as vegetable juice, organic fruits, and raw salads become acidic when consumed with negative emotions, but the pace of consumption will be rapid and erratic. Don't take your frustration out on your food by eating too quickly and not chewing properly. Instead, find a comfortable place to process your feelings, even if it means eating an hour later.

9. **Never eat because someone else wants you to eat.** Never forget that this is your body and your life and you never have to eat anything you don't want to eat! You decide what you wish to put into your body. The alternative is admitting a violation just like any other. You have the right to say no and stand up for yourself. You are not a receptacle for other people's projections and misplaced needs. You have likely experienced this many times: people will try various tactics to bully you into eating things you really don't want. If you have a personality that gives into this sort of bullying, you need to set very strong boundaries against it. Remember rule number one—eat only what is designated for you—and stick to it. If you have trouble saying no to others, think about why. You don't owe it to anyone to eat outside of what serves your highest good. If someone tries to pressure, bully, or guilt you into consuming unfit substances, this says more about that person's issues than about yours. Stay focused on your own. Stand strong. Believe in yourself. This is no small thing. You are saving your life here. You do not need to compromise your vision to appease others.

10. **Never eat after dinner.** Today, many people have unusual late-night habits as a result of deep stress. It's not uncommon for people to find themselves eating in a half-asleep state between sleep cycles—waking at 2 a.m., rummaging through the kitchen on a mini-binge, and going back to sleep, only to awaken the next morning feeling defeated and ashamed. If you make it perfectly clear to your conscious mind that you absolutely will not eat after dinner or late at night, your subconscious mind will be far less susceptible to this behavior.

11. **Your home is sacred.** If you are struggling with your body image, you might find it very difficult to stop playing that self-hating recording in your head. Try starting with your home. The size or fanciness of your home is irrelevant. What matters is that you care intimately for it. Your home is a reflection of you

and your self-esteem. Some homes are cluttered, some are creatively messy, some are spick-and-span, and some are a blend of these things. But I promise, you will be less susceptible to emotional eating and your life will run much more smoothly in a clean, orderly, nurturing environment. I admit, sometimes I go slightly out of my mind when I find myself cleaning our home incessantly (even with a housekeeper two days a week), but I make my home a priority and weave it into my children's lives as a priority as well. There are moments when I can enjoy the wholeness of my home as an extension of my own wholeness as I do small tasks such as picking up items off the floor, fluffing the pillows, or scrubbing dishes. Sometimes before the kids come home from school, I'll light the areas where they'll do their homework and strive to create a beautiful, loving, life-generating space for them to return to. No doubt their little antennae will detect this, and there will be less bickering and more healing energy in the wake of their own busy days at school. I think of my home as my garden, and there is a distinct pleasure to be had from tending it with care—and this transcends any feminist notions about woman in the home! So remember to connect with your sacred living space, and cultivate the same qualities of cleanliness in your home as you are striving for in your body.

12. Your mind is sacred. Sadly, people today typically leave their minds open to anything and everything. Guard your mind like a noble fortress. Your mind is a reservoir of the thoughts that will guide your life. A careless and indiscriminant mind will manifests in careless, indiscriminant words, actions, and behaviors. Many things bring filth into the mind. Some are so obvious but so common that they often go unnoticed. For example, consider all the vulgarities of tabloid news. To me, they are no better than porn, stimulating the basest appetites with a cacophony of mindless ogling, focusing mostly on women's bodies—*Look at what she's wearing! Look how skinny she is! She'd be hot if she lost ten pounds!* Suddenly things that were meaningless to you a moment earlier are the centerpiece of your thoughts. Suddenly you're pulled into the riptide of life-deteriorating messages dressed up as eye candy. Suddenly your head hurts from images flashing before your eyes at a million frames per second. Basically, you've lost your mind. You are a captive of the *S.S. Tabloid*, but you're addicted to this kind of captivity—it's an extreme form of stimulation that's completely endorsed by society. The same steps that will help you overcome your emotional eating will help liberate you from the cultural freak show that is today's mainstream media. Just as you wouldn't let just anyone into your home, don't let just anything into your mind.

13. Life is change. Your life will change with or without your active participation, in the direction of your consciousness. Wouldn't you rather be an active participant than an unconscious passenger of your own life? If you don't cultivate and expand your consciousness, it will shrink and atrophy. If you don't build healthy boundaries that filter out destructive elements and admit life-generating ones, all manner of alien forces will enter and wreak havoc on your body, your mind, and your spirit. There is no such thing as staying perfectly still. If you don't move, someone or something will move for you—and likely push you in a direction you don't want to go!

The Journey of the Hero

A hero is someone who has found or achieved or done something beyond the normal range of achievement or experience. A hero is someone who has properly given his life to something bigger than himself or other than himself. There are two types of [heroic] deeds. One deed is the hero who has performed a war act or physical act of heroism. Saving a life—that's a hero-act…and the other kind is the spiritual hero who has learned or found a mode of experiencing the supernormal range of spiritual life and come back and communicated it. It's a cycle. It's a going and returning that the hero-cycle represents. But it also represents a certain initiation ritual where a child has to give up his childhood and become an adult. He has to die you might say to his infantile personality, psyche and come back as a self-responsible adult. It's a fundamental experience that everyone has to undergo.

—Joseph Campbell

All the great ancient religions and philosophies offered their own esoteric guides for journeying into what we now call the unconscious mind. The great psychiatrist and thinker Carl Jung explained it in his definition of individuation. But today, only a relative few people ever experience or understand this journey. The ways into the unconscious reveal themselves only to those who truly wish to evolve to a higher state of consciousness. Such a state both predates and opposes separation consciousness, the dominant mindset the modern world.

Today we are deeply buried in untruths that we communally accept as normal. These norms are at the root of our modern condition, especially self-abuse in the form of addictive behavior. To delve into your unconsciousness and get to the root of your imbalances is to begin the Journey of the Hero. The average modern individual is internally shattered into more pieces than ever. If you are standing on the precipice of your unconscious with the dream of reclaiming your wholeness, your many shattered pieces stand to become your hero's bounty. Your duty is nothing short than to save yourself. Can you commit to this, or is there something more important for you to do?

You can spend years in therapy—whether Fruedian, Jungian, cognitive-behavioral, or otherwise—but you cannot expect true progress without practical applications for the reunification of the soul. Your behaviors are outgrowths of your beliefs. Your beliefs are outgrowths of not just what is conscious or even accessible in your subconscious, but also of all that lies repressed deep in your unconscious. Without delving deeply, you'll never gain any traction; you'll simply spin your wheels in desperation.

You stand now before a gateway. There are two choices before you: (1) enter, dig deep, and then pull yourself up from the depths; or (2) drown in acidic, stagnating emotional energy and eat yourself to oblivion.

Everywhere today, cells are mutating and the natural world is degenerating. That means you. You are part of the natural world that is under assault. And your self-abuse reflects the state of your soul. All the while, the world goes on pretending everything is working, making you feel you are the only one who cannot find satisfaction in it. The airbrushed newscasters smile and cheerily rattle off the day's latest horrors; commercials vie loudly and obnoxiously for our attention with useless products; and trends keep people in soul-deadening cycles of compulsive work and consumerism. We let the machinery of society think for us: it bombards us with images of what beauty, sex, fun, family, success—and even heroism—should look like, robbing us of our autonomy and better judgment.

You've seen the madness. Heck, you've lived it. You can accept the fact that the world is mad. Now it's time to accept the truth about the effects that the mad, mad world has had on you. You have spent a lifetime internalizing this madness with every bite you eat. You're suffering. And you want out. But the only way out is to delve into the deep, dark world of the unconscious and retrieve the heaps of information that have been hiding from you. You will pull up those dormant treasures from your unconsciousness into the light. Then you will integrate them into your whole being. You've been split into a million pieces, but with courage and determination you will fit those pieces back together again. It won't be easy, but this is the only kind of metamorphosis that will make your life worth living.

Self-abuse is rooted in places where most people are far too scared to go. I used to think that this didn't have to be the case, that there had to be an easier way. Alas, from my vantage point today, I don't believe that is possible. It takes the Journey of the Hero, which requires heroic courage, but will reward you with a hero's homecoming.

Be prepared for nothing short of a complete transformation. On a successful journey, you might embark feeling like a frightened child and return as a confident adult, or you might set out in the dark of night and step back into brilliant sunlight. But this is not child's play. Some people seek professional help with decades of training to help guide them safely through the treacherous terrain of their unconscious worlds. This can be helpful, depending on your needs and if you can find a guide whom you can trust. I have found the journey to be accessible to anyone who is strong enough to remain steadfast and true to his/her goal. Moreover, as I've said before, just because someone has a professional title or is in a position of authority doesn't mean he or she is to be trusted. Embark on this journey with your eyes wide open. Be brave, but respect your limits at any given stage. This is work for the powerful but peaceful warrior—indeed, for the hero that resides within you.

Exercise: Clean Your Closet, Literally!

To prepare for the journey ahead, you will need to unburden yourself of anything in your life that would weigh you down or hinder your progress. If it doesn't serve your highest purpose, it's gotta go. This is not an easy step. If you have a hard time parting with clothes you don't wear very often, this is going to be a tough one for you. For this very reason, your closet may be a great place to start! Go into your closet and select five to ten items you no longer need. With each item you toss away into a giveaway pile, imagine it representing a related aspect of your life that serves no good purpose. Maybe it was something you bought just because it was trendy, not because it flattered your figure or filled a gap in your wardrobe. Or perhaps it was to conform to some imagined dress code to hide your real self. These are deep issues. Letting go of each item with such ceremonial mindfulness will help prepare you for the kinds of leaps you'll soon be taking.

Exercise: Journey into the Unconscious

Please be forewarned that you may find this exercise to be intense. If at any stage the process becomes too much for you, simply lay the material aside for a time and resume when you feel ready to proceed. True healing takes time and advances bit by bit over a series of modest steps and the occasional leap. Stay true to your purpose. Only by working to reunify the shattered pieces of your soul, and then protecting that newfound wholeness, will you finally stop looking for satisfaction outside of yourself—from food, from the approval of others, from the numbers on a scale, and so on.

Now, take a deep breath, and be ready to release a lot of repressed energy! Take out a journal or a big pad of paper and make a list of all the things that you found frustrating in your life up until age 10. Next to each frustration, describe in detail the kinds of repressed emotions, thoughts, and behaviors you think it led to. Finally, where applicable, write down what you think your spirit is saying about it now. *Note: If you find yourself blocked, or unsure of how to begin, take a look at the excerpts from my own journal, on page 113, which I've included in order to demonstrate how this exercise worked for me.*

Let your spirit guide this exercise and give it completely free rein to express itself. Don't question or judge what comes up. Honor each memory, thought, and feeling that comes, even if you think it's ugly or petty. If it comes to mind, it belongs on the page. Do the same for ages 11–17, 18–28, 29–39, 40–55, 56–66, and 67–present, as applicable, adjusting the age brackets for relevance to your life. When you reach your current age, write down all the experiences that frustrate you today, how they are shaping your thoughts and behaviors, and how your spirit is interpreting them. Then review all your entries every day for ten days, filling in any additional details as they come to you, until these experiences are clearly restored to your consciousness.

Remember, on an inner journey, you don't have to worry about dismantling the world. Just trust that change happens from within. Do not be alarmed if you experience some growing pains as you draw up and shed old energies. It may be a distinct physical reaction, such as a series of night sweats where your body pours out the old energy through the skin; or trembling accompanied by tears or anger; or a sudden distaste for former habits, associations, or styles (e.g., you might transition away from office wear in favor of softer fabrics and more comfortable cuts). When you notice a change in your behavior or thought patterns, ask yourself, *What does this say about my evolution? How are my values shifting? Where am I now and where am I headed? What attracts or repels me? Whom do I wish to spend time with?* And so on. Remember, you summoned this change. Don't fear it. Enjoy it. Trust it. This is a great accomplishment. Be as present as you can be.

It's normal, on occasion, to find yourself feeling as though you are backsliding during this process. I still experience this from time to time. Sometimes I don't realize how social standards still grip me, so I'll feel sad, discouraged, or engage in some erratic activity because I can't hear my spirit is telling me to let go. The fears creep in: *Where will I go from here if I release that? Will I eventually become a total outcast? Am I being disrespectful to tradition? Who am I to think my spirit is right when so many other voices contradict it?* Those sneaky self-doubts and concerns block my growth. I don't have all the answers, nor should I put that kind of pressure on myself. I might be wrong—that's okay. But my childhood programming tells me that's not okay, that if I am going to be an authority even over myself, I must expand as big as the universe in order to provide the answers for every possible context. I'd better be right. That's the social programming speaking, and it rules me only until I recognize the fears and self-doubts for what they are, release them, and move on. Find one foothold after the next, and then settle on a place to camp until the next call to change comes. Each stage of the journey is its own reward!

A Lesson in Values

The values you were raised with are not necessarily the values you want to take with you into the next phase of your metamorphosis. Consider them very carefully: they are birthed from your frustrations and wiring, not necessarily from your highest ideals. If you consider the behaviors of most fanatics who get all puffed up about their values of chastity, charity, love, patriotism, humility, religious devotion, and so on, watch how they live their lives and you'll see their true values. All too often, here is where their hearts really are: materialism, sexual gratification, power, physical appearance, social approval, financial success, fame and influence. We all believe we have strong values, but how many of us actually believe in them enough to live them day in and day out?

How do we begin to slough off our old, socially programmed values and rebuild our lives on real, life-affirming ones? Our values are not necessary moral. People often confuse these two terms. I grew up going to church in a family with married parents and fine possessions. I was taught chastity and I was taught the Bible. I also learned that the body is a girl's calling card, and that the death of an American teenager will draw a lot more airtime on the news than will the death of thousands of Indians in an earthquake. I learned that getting an education is valuable, but that being a sexy celebrity is more valuable.

In short, my early education and life experience instilled a set of values in me that would determine many of my subsequent choices and behaviors. These distinctly life-deteriorating values were intimately tied to my self-abuse. They would eat away at my soul, and no amount of purging could silence those dreadful voices that ran my life.

It's kind of ironic. In my youth I was taught lot of rules about wholesome, godly ways to live, and yet what I actually absorbed from my matrix were unwholesome, ungodly, yet seemingly necessary values for survival. Today, without even trying, I can simply be aware of the way living things function and thrive, and trust the values that now naturally direct my life.

I had to learn the Bible inside and out as a kid, and now many of those verses make far more sense to me than they ever did then. I am reminded of one very appropriate verse that I didn't understand back then as I understand it now: *Do not lay up for yourselves treasures on earth, where moth and rust destroy and where thieves break in and steal, but lay up for yourselves treasures in heaven, where neither moth nor rust destroys and where thieves do not break in and steal. For where your treasure is, there your heart will be also.* (Matt: 6, 19-21)

See, all that Bible study wasn't wasted on me! It was just taught by people who didn't understand it themselves to children who had far more distracting influences in their lives. So the verses sat like dead words on deaf ears.

Exercise: Hold Your Values Up to the Light

Go through your values, one by one. Here's how. Ask yourself the following questions:

1. What do I respond to most strongly?
2. What do I spend my time, money, and energy on?
3. What have I wanted most in life up until now?

Make a list of all these things and notice what has really mattered most to you. Don't be shy or embarrassed. You can tear the list up and throw it away later, if you want. I recommend you look at it every now and then to remind you of your values at this point in your life and how they can evolve.

Then imagine or write down all the life-deteriorating effects of those values. Write down what they do to your body. How do they make you feel? How do they affect your thinking, your digestion, your muscles, your sleep patterns, your friendships, your environment? How does each value affect your power, your clarity, and your creativity?

This brings to mind another great biblical quote: *So every good tree bears good fruit, but the bad tree bears bad fruit. A good tree cannot produce bad fruit, nor can a bad tree produce good fruit. Every tree that does not bear good fruit is cut down and thrown into the fire. So then, you will know them by their fruits.* (Matt 7, 17-20)

In other words, a choice that sprouts from life-deteriorating values will never, ever bear good fruit. So if you want to enjoy good fruit, you will need to undergo a deep shift in values and, when you are ready, discard the bad ones altogether. It's not dogma or religion, it's the universal law of nature. What are you values? What they were yesterday does not have to be what they will become today or tomorrow. Change them at your own pace. Let them evolve organically as your consciousness expands. Again, this is not a race. Simply exercise awareness and allow the forward momentum to carry you naturally to your next step.

I won't tell you what your values should be. That is personal. I have no doubt that the best values have always resided deep within you, and that with some conscious cultivation they will help you grow in a more life-generating direction. With strong values, you will not only bear strong fruit, but you will be strong enough to withstand outside disapproval.

Forgiveness

"Forgiveness"—like "self-love" and "consciousness"—is a popular term that is meaningless until you truly experience it. Most people, and particularly extreme self-abusers, tend to validate their behavior by laying blame on something or someone else—such as bad parenting, childhood abuse, divorce, a tragic death, a missed opportunity, etc. All self-abuse comes from the past.

The fact is that in a world of separation consciousness, young people absorb a shocking amount of adult neurosis and pathology. Most people who reach adulthood in this culture are far from balanced human beings, much less fit for parenthood. They have accumulated a lot of frustrations, disappointments, perversions, and bad habits that color everything they think, feel, and do.

I just wish someone had told me at age fourteen or fifteen that the adult world was crazy, that the whole value system was a bunch of nonsense, and not to think too much of it. I wish someone had told me that I was not the only one suffering inside, that even those who appear to have it all together and know exactly what they are doing are in fact carrying a whole lot of pain and confusion. This is pretty much what I tell any teenager who comes to me with their anxieties (parents be warned).

I'm not suggesting children should be disrespectful toward adults. Every single human being deserves respect, and children need guidance from adults they can trust. But I am suggesting that young people not remove necessary boundaries in order to fall automatically into line with an adult perspective. An adult's age, professional status, or guardianship over a child is no indication of his or her inherent wisdom. Young people need to know what to look for in a leader. Some of the most seemingly well-intentioned adults take children in deadly directions, often for lack of direction, but just as frequently because the child follows the adult along a widely accepted but destructive path. Aren't so many acceptable paths deceptively destructive? Yet there is rarely an alternative example and society is slow to recognize its misjudgments until it is far too late.

Our mainstream world is not fit for children, and most adults are broken children trapped in adult bodies. I have met few who aren't. If you are a young person reading this, it is important to have a compassionate heart full of respect for adults, but be aware that "adult" is in no way synonymous with "safe" or "wise." It takes a great deal of focus, consciousness, love, and determination for a person to truly mature and come of age in this world. If only this were a prerequisite for parenthood!

Now that you can no longer blame the past or your parents, you must work with the present. Is someone abusing you in some way? They are? Well then, you are no longer seven years old and powerless. Find a way to banish them from your life. Is someone telling you you're not good enough or giving you backhanded insults? Simply confront them or send them away. Seek help and support from people you trust, if necessary. Is the person you hold responsible for your pain inflicting pain on you currently, or are you clinging tightly to an old grudge?

There is no doubt that you must have boundaries— healthy, strong boundaries that keep out life-deteriorating forces and values. Your boundaries should be diaphanous for some and like steel for others. Only you know how to customize those individual boundaries. But if you are holding grievances from the past as a defense or an excuse to avoid taking responsibility for yourself, you are only cheating yourself.

I think the ability of traditional therapy to help pull you out of abusive and violent experiences is limited. Only by finally recognizing that those adults are the fruits of an undeniably life-deteriorating and foolish world could I stop blaming and begin forgiving. Few actions in life are as personally empowering and liberating as forgiveness. Imagine all the emotional energy you could spend on more worthwhile pursuits, if you could just bring yourself to forgive!

We peaceful warriors can either stand around in self-pity or confront the real culprit: the value system of the modern world. With this realization, our blame and anger can yield to genuine sadness for a world of suffering. Only in such a spirit of compassion and forgiveness—for ourselves as well as for others—can we start to piece ourselves back together.

Exercise: Put Humpty Dumpty Back Together Again

You have now identified the pieces of yourself that have been unfairly banished to your unconsciousness and brought them back into your conscious life with love, appreciation, and a great big "welcome home" sign. And you've now erected strong boundaries to protect your highest good. Now it's time to put the pieces back together again. Here are the steps of reunification:

1. Care for each broken piece that you've recovered from the depths as you would a newborn baby. Protect it. Nurture it.

2. Mend the body with clean, alkaline, nourishing food and a new appreciation for what belongs in the body.

3. Mend your mind with human thinking—not mutant thinking, abusive thinking, inherited thinking, or programmed thinking. See the difference.

4. Accept the freedom to build yourself and your life anew with life-generating values and the choices that spring from them. Acknowledge that it is fully within your power to make honest, life-affirming choices at every turn, to stop suffering at your own hands.

5. Be innovative where necessary. Don't let anything stand in your way or start making excuses. Nothing stands in your way. Find the solutions. Focus on what you can do right now,

today, not on what you fear you won't be able to do tomorrow.

6. When you feel moments of weakness, ask yourself: Why would I want to abuse myself? Why would I want to stuff myself? Can't I see that emotional eating is a form of violent self-abuse? Why would I want to harm myself when protection and healing is what I need? What is my inner voice trying to say that I may be ignoring? What would happen if I were to be myself and not what others have programmed me to be? Who would reject me? Why? What's the worst-case scenario? What's the best-case scenario? Hold that image of your best self and your best life.

7. Remember, to slay the dragon of emotional eating takes discipline and hard work: it's a way of life. We live in a world of passivity and sloth. We are hypnotized and infantilized by a culture that would have us sucking on the bottle of consumerism like a bunch of addicts, lured by feelings of inadequacy, all our lives. Sometimes it's hard to remember that the world is insane, not us. Don't fall into that trap!

8. Maintain the cleanliness of your cells, your home, and your mind. Be extra vigilant against compromising influences as you transition from separation consciousness to unity consciousness. Protect your initial vulnerability, and know that you will become clearer and stronger with each conscious step.

9. Take responsibility for every part of your life. Say what you mean, mean what you say, accept the consequences. Don't be afraid to fail. If you stumble, get back up, dust yourself off, and pick up where you left off.

10. Remember to savor the rushes of unparalleled joy and recognition that come with reviving your spirit. You are both the star and the creative director of your own life. You are a brilliant visionary, preparing and fusing together all the various parts of yourself for the role of a lifetime!

Conclusion

The average person's relationship with food today is complex and misguided. Sadly, that's the state of the civilized world, and for whatever deep-seated reasons, some of us struggle with it more than others. But no matter who you are or how acute your imbalances are, emotional eating corrodes your life at every level.

At the most basic level, an overeater's bones and intestines ache with excess gas pressure. Constipation causes migraines and depression. Yeast makes you reach for sugars and starches. Chemical addiction to modern foods makes quitting overeating as hard as quitting heroine or cigarettes. Emotional eating is a physiological condition with roots in emotional brokenness, which makes escape extremely difficult.

But now you finally know what you want: a life free of harmful social programs, free of accumulated waste, free of personal drama, free of self-hatred, free of all the nonsense that makes an endless frustration. Look deep enough within yourself and you'll know, truly know, what you want and what you don't want.

When *The Secret* swept the nation, were people excited about the possibility of reclaiming inner balance, confidence, wisdom, respect for the planet and its inhabitants? Gosh no, they were frothing at the mouth for the opportunity to rub the magic lantern and wish for money, cars, sex appeal, vacations, and all other manner of pie-in-the-sky escapes that they are programmed to want, that keep them in cycles of insatiable cravings. As ever, the idea of change is always attractive—if it's easy.

If you *really* want to change, to harvest a new crop of cells in your body and a whole new outlook on life, it's time to turn and reseed the soil. How hard will it be? Well, that depends on how badly you want it. If you are too caught up worrying about what other people might think, you will have a hard time.

The more you desire to be free, the more fuel you will have for this endeavor. It can happen fairly swiftly, or it can require many takes and retakes before you gain momentum. The fact is, you are where you are and you cannot force yourself to journey onward if you're not ready. There's no point in resisting yourself and setting yourself up to feel like a failure. Better to take baby steps.

Overeating shares much in common with alcoholism and other behaviors of excessive consumption. At the root is a desire for an alternate reality, one with less pain and more freedom. This is the inclination of a spirit that has been broken and muzzled by rules that suffocate human nature. During every moment of your life, your spirit is desperately trying to communicate with you, attempting to point out that which must be changed for your life to work as it can and should. It is possible to change. You just have to listen attentively and implement change accordingly.

If you do not love your life, you will always be looking for an alternate reality. Start creating the life you love by doing whatever it takes to retrieve those lost pieces of your soul and bring them back together. Shake off the chains of social conditioning; let your spirit free. When your spirit calls, pick up. Don't ignore it by stuffing your mouth with another bite. There is no difference between this and knocking back another drink at the bar. Sooner or later, you will have to wake up the next morning and face reality with a great big hangover. At a certain point you're going to reach the bottom of the carton, the bottom of the bag, the bottom of the bowl. Then what? Then you're just dissatisfied with your life *and* upset with yourself for taking the path of least resistance. As hard as changing your life might seem, in the long run it is much easier than maintaining this devastating cycle of self-abuse. You've been stuck here for too long. You know it well enough.

Your life, your joy, your ability to express yourself really matter! I cannot impress this upon you enough. You have been shackled by so many limiting beliefs. They will only tighten, further choking off your body and your spirit, with each self-silencing choice. Communication can save you: listen to your spirit, respond to its wisdom, go where you need to go to find yourself anew.

The journey back to balance and wholeness is far better than any alternate reality that can be achieved through substance abuse. With each thoughtful, courageous adjustment, you will feel exciting shifts in your life! Eventually, you will experience moment-to-moment, day-by-day, year-by-year sovereignty. You will serve your inner balance first and foremost, and protect it from destabilizing forces. You will feel reborn.

Don't worry, the food will still be there—better than ever, tastier than ever. The difference is that you will eat what your body truly need and desires. You'll enjoy beautiful plates of fresh, hydrating, nurturing, delicious dishes comprised of nature's finest delicacies. You will have your fill. You'll enjoy these foods socially and during quiet nights alone. All the pleasures of food will be there, and there's no pleasure for a healthy spirit quite like natural, fresh food. You will no longer use food to shut yourself up, shut yourself down, or escape your reality. You will be present when you partake of food, glorious food. With all of this comes the joie de vivre that is every human being's birthright: a whole and balanced spirit partnered with a beautiful, vibrant body and a healthy appetite!

My Journey into the Unconscious

To give you a sense of how the Journey into the Unconscious works (see page 98), I will share a sampling of entries from my own journal. You will find my frustrations in bold type, and the repressed emotions and imbalanced behaviors that I believe those experiences wired me for in italics. Remember, this represents only a sampling of my jottings, spanning my life only up until my early twenties. You may treat this intimate glimpse of my personal journey as a rough guide to help jump-start you on your own journey. But first, I would like to state for the record that, while these many deep frustrations broke my soul into pieces and have taken most of my adult life to repair, I am not complaining or forgetting all the wonderful things I have experienced in my life. Despite my frustrations, I would not have wished for another life or another family. I am grateful for the journey that has brought me here. I sincerely hope that you, too, will draw strength from this exercise and make it your own.

AGES 1–10:

I felt like I was in a cage at the mercy of my parents' plans.

This wired me for confinement. My natural sense of freedom was repressed.

I felt at the mercy of my older brother's whims: Is he going to be nice to me today? Will he play with me? Will he make me feel good about myself?

This wired me to seek attention and approval from boys. It repressed my natural self-acceptance and self-confidence.

I picked up on tensions in my family members. There was no natural joy.

This wired me for imbalanced relationships. It repressed my natural desire to exchange unconditional love with those I lived *with. I think my spirit picked up on the fact that they had given up their authority to others.*

I didn't understand how the world worked, only how our world at home functioned. Our little world seemed like a desert island, disconnected and apart.

This wired me for confusion and self-doubt. It repressed the natural sense of connection and community a child naturally longs for.

I had no sense of my place in the world, only of my place in my family, characterized by being my parents' daughter at the club and on expeditions. Their friends showered me with compliments in order to make polite conversation and to keep up appearances.

From here on out, this wired me to let others determine my self-worth, based on the things these people praised and valued most about me—my appearance, mainly. This robbed me of my natural unselfconsciousness, which is every child's birthright.

I was left in the hands of dangerous family members for a prolonged period during which I was exposed to devastating abuse.

This wired me to assume that people were perverted, violent, and generally hiding behind false facades of goodness and Godliness.

There were fights at home. Big ones. Then everything would normalize and everyone would act as though they never said or did anything out of the ordinary. I didn't understand that. I witnessed and experienced real pain, but then it was invalidated.

This wired me for extreme anxiety and repressed emotion. I saw human emotion as something that could be spent, shattered, devalued.

AGES 11–17:

Note: I'm getting anxious just contemplating these years. It's almost too emotional for me to pull this time period up. I can feel my whole body reacting, physically resisting this exercise—from the throbbing in my legs to the tension in my neck.

I was scared in middle school. I had friends but they were unpredictable.

This wired me to distrust my peers. It repressed natural friendship.

I didn't like focusing so much on how I looked, but I didn't want to be an outcast.

This wired me for intense self-critique and female competition.

I didn't really understand what was expected of me academically. Was I smart? I didn't really know. What if I failed? Would I be bagging groceries for the rest of my life?

This wired me for academic insecurity and stress. It repressed my natural curiosity, my natural intelligence, my natural thirst for knowledge.

I grew up affluent but I had no real sense of the connection between education and occupation. I had no sense of connection to the past or continuity with the future. My world was just a vast landscape called Los Angeles where some people made it and some didn't, and "making it" was a strange, unpredictable mystery all its own.

This wired me to accept our culture of disconnectedness (or separation consciousness). I became a prisoner of my confusion and thus relinquished my power of discretion to the juggernaut. This repressed my spirit and my innate powers of understanding.

I felt like an alien trying to fit in. It seemed everything required manipulation—being popular, going to the mall, attracting the boy you liked, surviving at home.

Here is where I finally gave up on being myself. This wired me to hide all my real qualities and dress up for this stage of life.

My family members and school environment grew ever more unpredictable and disconcerting, so I devised an escape plan: boarding school.

This taught me to run away, far away, to escape my problems.

As life away from home allowed me to find a sense of direction, I lost touch with my parents and brother. The family seemed to disintegrate, or at least I became more like an offshoot of their world than a central member.

This wired me for increased self-doubt. I repressed the unspeakable—the conflict, the pain, the confusion. I piled on the armor and desensitized myself. Some family members were so emotionally dangerous that, if I didn't protect myself, I would spend every day in tears.

My father's health declined rapidly with a series of strokes and growing senility. This scared me. I didn't know what to do with him or with myself. I wanted to help but always seemed to be in the way. I kept asking myself: How could a person live a full life and have it all come down to eating dinner with strangers in a home for the elderly?

At this point I think I started to fully repress my innate sense of right and wrong, because right and wrong didn't seem to apply to anything in this upside-down reality.

Food was a huge part of my life at boarding school and it was making me fat. Why did my once lithe form have to expand and ruin my appearance? Why was it so hard to get dressed? Why did food have to do that to the body? Why did this issue occupy all of my thoughts? I was either feeling hungry, eating, or dressing up for a school event or church service that would be followed with more of the sickening foods that I couldn't resist.

This wired me to distrust food, distrust my body, distrust the purpose of life at boarding school. I sensed that there were all these rules and expectations for women, that there was a double standard, but I felt powerless against them.

I felt sick in body and spirit, I had to visit my father in a depressing elderly home, and all that anyone seemed to care about was being attractive, getting an education, and getting a job. Beyond that, no one seemed to know what life was about.

This wired me to devalue life itself.

I read my Bible and reflected back on my Christian upbringing. I hoped to find answers in some coded fashion there. I took my religious studies very seriously and considered theology as a vocation. But if religion seemed to hold value, it also seemed full of hypocrisy. There were the believers and the non-believers, yet I could not say that I belonged to either group.

I felt caged by all sorts of limitations I couldn't name. Despite my youth and the world being wide open to me, I didn't like my options. They seemed so limiting. No life options appealed to me—even the glamorous or aristocratic ones. I was reduced to thinking of success in terms of materialism, but it left me feeling empty.

My father died while I was away at school. My mother told me to stay at school. I couldn't comprehend a life that ended in silence. After all that time together, he was just gone, and the world went on without him.

This wired me to feel the triteness of life. What was it all for—all the drama, all the emotion, all the effort to keep up appearances—if this was how it ended?

I felt horrible in my clothes. Growing up, I'd always been told I was pretty, thin, and stylish like my mother, but how could I feel good about myself now? I had terrible acne, tree trunks for legs, curtains for hair. I went for long runs but my jeans were still too tight. I didn't want to spend the rest of my life hating my body.

I realized that if I couldn't stop eating, I could at least throw up the food that was making me sick. This felt like a solution until I realized that I was still feeling ugly and sick, yet I couldn't make myself stop throwing up. This wired me for self-hatred.

I did really well in school but I still couldn't conceive of my future. All I knew was that I needed to fill some kind of role.

This wired me to seek answers from others. I limited my ideas about the future to what my school and college counselors deemed viable professions.

We weren't affluent anymore. I was too scared to ask about our financial status, but I soon learned I'd have to find a way to pay for a university education myself.

This wired me for survival at all costs. Social acceptance via financial and material success remained more important than integrity and honesty.

AGES 18 - 22:

At New York University, I had no idea where to go or what to do. Classes seemed random and there was so little guidance. I felt completely isolated and alone. I scoured the papers for work and went on job interviews.

This wired me further for self-doubt. Intimidated by the social paradigm, I relinquished self-expression and self-direction. I let myself be carried by a tide I didn't understand. It was like the moment in a tug-o-war when you just cannot hang on any longer and you surrender the rope to the team pulling you in the other direction.

I attracted the eye of a wealthy businessman. He gave me a job as his personal assistant. It paid really well. All I had to do was pretend to like him and take care of his business. He was always trying to kiss me and I was always trying to dart around his advances. He gave me the creeps, but it paid for NYU and the expenses of being a girl.

This wired me for more self-loathing and self-deception, and a further relinquishing of power. I started to see how an attractive young woman could take the path of least resistance. I lost another piece of myself: my integrity. This was a form of spiritual suicide. Yet, I convinced myself that working for this man was not only necessary, but also dignified compared to some of the other paths taken by my peers.

There was no one to stop me on this self-destructive path. I had no one to turn to for guidance when I was clearly lacking in certain critical values.

This wired me to blame others—to blame my employer, my mother, my youth—anyone and anything to avoid taking responsibility for my actions.

There was no consistent joy, no reliable safety, no light to lead me out of the darkness and deception. I became a slave to the gym and maintained my disordered eating patterns. I still despised my body. I continued working in office cubicles, paying dues, gazing up the corporate ladders. This way of life seemed the only option for a responsible member of upwardly mobile society, so I joined the ranks of those college grads who would spend their lives indoors in jobs they hated.

This wired me for a limited, trapped existence, devoid of any real joy. Rather than go after my dreams, I contented myself with small indulgences, such as dinner out, a good haircut, or a new purchase that offered a momentary high.

I hit rock bottom.

My spirit cried out for help at the highest pitch. I finally started listening. I knew I had to change, really change…

* * *

If there is an overriding theme that runs through all of my frustrations, it is disconnectedness: not fitting into the social mold, living for the self in meaningless isolation. Of course, I still experience frustrations to this day, and my journey is ongoing, but this exercise has helped me to open up to myelf and expand my spirit immeasurably. As you embark on your own journey into the past, you will likely recall many points of disconnect, isolation, and shame. Let it be a comfort, a source of courage, to know that these experiences are what have brought you to this point of self-discovery. As long as you reconnect with your spirit, you can never be truly alone, and there is no greater journey than the journey back to wholeness.

Acknowledgments

This book was conceived as far back as my junior year in high school, when I started to become aware of my fraught relationship with food. Instead of honoring food as a source of nutrition and joy, I was reaching for it as a weapon, a suit of armor, a hiding place, a muzzle.

Since then, countless personal and professional encounters with emotional eating have offered me a multifaceted perspective on this important topic. Thus, I would like to take this opportunity to honor my many friends and clients whose openness about their suffering helped me better understand my own and expanded my perception to the degree that this project required.

This book would have been twice as long and half as clear were it not for Anna Bliss, my genius editor and easily one of the finest minds in the business. After five books and countless other projects together, she has fully earned my deepest gratitude and admiration several times over.

Thank you to cover designer and web savant Tim Roberts, who—along with his visionary team at Crucial Networking—created the Detoxtheworld.com website. Thanks also to Gerardo Somoza for the cover image!

A special thanks to my family—to my husband, Lawrence, and to my children, Thandi and Tommy, for their constant support.

Last but in many ways most, I would like to thank Ana Ladd-Griffin for the tireless work she does to make sure Detoxtheworld.com and all its many parts run smoothly day in and day out.

CPSIA information can be obtained at www.ICGtesting.com
Printed in the USA
LVOW110315260412

279057LV00002B/259/P